Poetry In Motion

North & East London
Edited by Claire Tupholme

 Young**Writers**

First published in Great Britain in 2004 by:
Young Writers
Remus House
Coltsfoot Drive
Peterborough
PE2 9JX
Telephone: 01733 890066
Website: www.youngwriters.co.uk

SB ISBN 1 84460 379 2

Foreword

This year, the Young Writers' 'Poetry In Motion' competition proudly presents a showcase of the best poetic talent selected from over 40,000 up-and-coming writers nationwide.

Young Writers was established in 1991 to promote the reading and writing of poetry within schools and to the youth of today. Our books nurture and inspire confidence in the ability of young writers and provide a snapshot of poems written in schools and at home by budding poets of the future.

The thought effort, imagination and hard work put into each poem impressed us all and the task of selecting poems was a difficult but nevertheless enjoyable experience.

We hope you are as pleased as we are with the final selection and that you and your family continue to be entertained with *Poetry In Motion North & East London* for many years to come.

Contents

Convent Of Jesus & Mary Language College

The Compton School

The King Alfred School

University College School

The Poems

My Fantasy Fairy

Twinkling wings and eyes of blue,
I'm fascinated by her colours,
Pink, blue and maroon.

I watch her fly, night and day
And see that she is very gay.
Her pearly white teeth and little blue shoes
And hair like silk,
I wonder where such beauty comes from.

Her little pink top and rosy pink cheeks,
Her little red lips
And small dancing hips.

Swinging her wand she whispers 'Abracadabra,'
And in a little puff of smoke,
She disappears from sight.

Was I dreaming? Was she real?

Gemma Graham (12)
Convent Of Jesus & Mary Language College

The Sun

The sun is big,
Just like a pig
That's in the sky,
So very high.
It shines all day
And shines all night,
It always shines its brightest light.
When it is near it is as big as a tree,
But when it is far it's as small as a leaf.
The sun is like many stars
Which could never ever fit into a vase.

Shaneka Rodney (12)
Convent Of Jesus & Mary Language College

The Seasons

Spring, the season of new life,
When the flowers bloom
And the vulnerable lambs and chicks
Make their presence known to all,
You can tell it's spring.

Summer, the season for shorts and T-shirts,
When the weather is flaming hot,
The ice cream van comes daily
And the summer holidays begin,
You can tell it's summer.

Autumn, the season that prepares us for winter,
When the squirrels hide their treasures,
The kids go back to school and
The leaves go mud-coloured and fall,
You can tell it's autumn.

Winter, the season of cold weather,
When the days grow shorter,
Trees are bare, nature falls asleep
And Christmas draws near,
You can tell it's winter.

Felicia Silberhorn-Armantrading (15)
Convent Of Jesus & Mary Language College

Mummy

M y mum is loving and caring, but sometimes more
     annoying than me
U nder my mum's skin, her heart grows as big as the sea
M ums love their children but my mum loves me the most
M y mum comforted me when I was little, every time I thought
     there was a ghost
Y ellow is my mum's colour hair, it represents the sun and she
     is the sun, my one and only loving mum.

Shannen Ashcroft (11)
Convent Of Jesus & Mary Language College

My Special Holiday

I could feel my feet sinking in the sand
Turkey is a magical land
The town of Gumbet was friendly and dear
The sun was so bright, the sea was so clear

The hotel pool was the place we played every day
My brother annoyed me and got in the way
The snorkelling was cool, the sea was so blue
We loved it so much and so would you

The Turkish food was so different
We experimented each night
The dishes were exotic
The prices just right

We played crazy golf in the gardens so green
The flowers were beautiful and the grounds so clean
My mum watched us with a cool drink in her hand
Turkey really is a magical land.

Roisin Campbell (11)
Convent Of Jesus & Mary Language College

Life

You're born, you die;
You eat, you cry,
You love, you hate,
You kiss, you date.

As you get older, your emotions go wild,
You're growing into an adult, you're not a child.
You'll soon love someone, someone will love you,
The time will come, there's another child,
But this time it's not you,
These are the things you'll have to go through.

Lanrae Nyack (11)
Convent Of Jesus & Mary Language College

Grandad

Grandad we love you
Grandad we care
Now that you're gone
Our lives will be bare

My nan, Mary
Your loving wife
Is happy that she
Could share in your life

Your girls can take heart
No pain was suffered
And you are now
Reunited with your mother

Your memory will live on
Deep in our minds
Although there was no time
To say our goodbyes

On Good Friday this year
We all shed some tears
We know Jesus died
But so did you, the nicest guy

With a smile on his face
And paint on his clothes
That's how you knew him
When he went down the road.

Alice Smith (12)
Convent Of Jesus & Mary Language College

Teddy Bears

Eight little teddy bears
Eat honey at eleven;
One has sticky paws,
That leaves only seven.

Seven little teddy bears
Together playing tricks;
One is very sleepy,
That leaves only six.

Six little teddy bears,
Like to swim and dive;
One decides to climb a tree,
That leaves only five.

Five little teddy bears
Are polishing the floor;
One sits down to have a rest,
That leaves only four.

Four little teddy bears
Have a picnic by the sea;
One is sleeping in the sand,
That leaves only three.

Three little teddy bears
Play all morning through;
One is skipping with a rope,
That leaves only two.

Two little teddy bears
Reading in the sun;
One has finished with her book,
That leaves only one.

Mukky Nnoruka (12)
Convent Of Jesus & Mary Language College

We Are Love

As two star-crossed lovers,
Our fates were set,
Against the threats of others,
In secret we met.

Our parents made battle,
Whilst we made love,
Swords with hatred did rattle,
Shower your kisses from above.

All things big and all things small,
Over nature we will tower,
Our love is the greatest of them all,
This love will keep gaining power.

When you look at the skies,
Remember, the stars are our eyes,
Wherever you go, whatever you do,
Our love will always travel with you.

Zynab Maria Al-Kadhim (14)
Convent Of Jesus & Mary Language College

School

Mental, mutilating maths
Maths, maths drives me mad
Maths, maths, always bad
Maths, maths, terrible toil
Maths, maths, makes me boil
Enrolling, exciting English
English, English, would never want to miss
English, English, it is so much bliss
English, English is such fun
English, English for everyone.

Janet Okwesa (11)
Convent Of Jesus & Mary Language College

Never Forget

Never forget that I love you,
The way you make me smile;
I have something to tell you,
I am going away for a while.

Never forget that you've touched me,
Something neither of us will forget;
I'm trying to get away from me,
What happened between us is nothing to regret.

Never forget the way we talked,
The one thing we were both good at;
Memories come from everywhere we've walked,
Even the places where we've quietly sat.

Never forget the things we shared,
The things that brought us together;
Things like the love and pain that we've beared,
These will stay with us forever.

Kimberley Barrett (15)
Convent Of Jesus & Mary Language College

The Tropical Seas

The pineapple shores
That rush through my life
And even though they are memories
They stab like a knife

The fish that swim by
Although the tide was low
My thoughts were ripe
Like a precious mango.

Luisa Celentano (11)
Convent Of Jesus & Mary Language College

Every Time In A Precious Mind

Every time you turn around,
Every time you fear.
Every time you see a child,
Every time you will see a tear.

Every time you see this tear,
Every time a child cries.
Every time you think,
Every time you take a few sighs.

Every time you take these sighs,
Every time you wonder.
'Every time, why is it they cry?'
Every time you sit and ponder.

Every time the solution passes through,
Every time you try to find a way.
Every time you try to help,
Every time you try to give this child a better day.

Every time you try to give this child a better day,
Every time you might say,
It takes more than one person to stop a war,
But no, it just starts with one.

Hayley-Marie Loughran (12)
Convent Of Jesus & Mary Language College

School, School, School!

I changed my school one year ago,
To secondary, you should know.
From my school I write this poem,
I sit at home, moan and groan.
Too much homework, I cry why, why, why?
I must fly to get it done,
But is it really the right one?

Back to school in uniform,
In I go dressed in blue,
So many things to do,
Meet my friends, find the teachers I need to see,
It's about my homework, it's hard to me.

I find myself in registration, getting the register called,
I come last, it's a long time till it gets to me.
It's 9:05, boo hoo, first lesson, what am I going to do?
Forgotten my RE book again.

With double RE over, it's time for break, whoopee!
Up to the canteen for a sausage roll, oh, big queue!

With break over and my sausage roll eaten,
It's time for English, yeah! we're doing a display.

With double English over, it's time for lunch,
Yeah! it's early lunch today.

With lunch over, only four lessons to go
Then it's time for home, hey, hey!

Katie Walsh (12)
Convent Of Jesus & Mary Language College

Spring!

Spring, spring has come out to play,
Spring, spring, brightens the day.
The lovely breeze gives our hair a fine spring style,
We unwrap ourselves from the winter shawls
And prance around in our light thin clothes.

Winter, winter has gone away,
Winter, winter has lost the fight,
The cold, icy wind has gone again
And let the warmer spring sun shine away.

Spring, spring is so much fun,
But I can't wait till summer comes,
Summer, summer, come our way,
So we can have a longer day.

Roxanne Swan (13)
Convent Of Jesus & Mary Language College

Holidays

When I go on holiday, I focus on the beach,
Picking shells and chasing crabs,
Then bathing in saltwater.

When I go on holiday, I tend to have great fun,
Mum says I should work instead, but I always object.

When I go on holiday, I never like the end,
'Cause . . . the end is when I have to leave and get on a freezing plane.

When I go on holiday, I try to hide my passport,
So when we go, I don't have my passport and that way I stay
                                                      till it's found.

Maria Ramdeen (12)
Convent Of Jesus & Mary Language College

In The Jungle

The king of the jungle, tough yet so elegant,
Strolling through the overgrowth, spying on its prey.
Its mane is so frizzled, long and bushy,
The lion looks so soft but so frightening as well.
He lurks in the grass and wanders by the trees,
Passing by the elephants, deer and leaves.
Down by the waterside, looking for a drink,
A stream that flows so far, so long and deep.
Troops of monkeys swinging by,
The lion grinds his teeth.
His eyes glued on the deer, so juicy and so sweet,
The birds flying over, his ideal piece of meat.
Well then Mr Lion King, the jungle's biggest beast,
You growl, you roar and kill your prey
And that makes you my big king.

Joanne Rooney (12)
Convent Of Jesus & Mary Language College

Chocolate!

C adbury's chocolate, yum, yum, yum, divine.
H ot chocolate is even finer.
O h how I love to eat chocolate nearly every day.
C homping and chewing, rotting my teeth away.
O nly I can never stop loving chocolate, not any day.
L ots of different types, that as you eat you feel relaxed.
A ll of them I like but my favourite is Galaxy.
T hey all taste great, well most of them do.
E ver, if I ever had to live without chocolate, I just don't
    know what I'd do!

Katie Silmon (13)
Convent Of Jesus & Mary Language College

The Four Seasons

The sweet cool breeze
Of the spring season,
The pink blossom falling off the trees.

The hot blazing sun
Of the summer season,
The fiery heat beating your skin.

The brown and orange leaves
Of the autumn season,
Crunching underneath your feet.

The freezing cold ice
Of the winter season,
Cracking as you walk along the street.

Gina-Marie Richards (12)
Convent Of Jesus & Mary Language College

The Fairground

'Oh yes! We're here!'
I say with a delightful cheer
I'll go up the side
Then down the inflatable slide!
I go through the air
The wind whipping my hair!

Oh what rapture and joy!
Let's try and hook a toy
I'll go on the trampoline now
I soar through the air and shout *'Wow!'*
I've had fun at the fair
And so has my hair!

Alessia Moriero (12)
Convent Of Jesus & Mary Language College

Chocolate

Smooth and creamy,
It melts on your tongue,
Heavenly, dreamy,
It's incredibly fun!

Dark chocolate, white chocolate,
Milk chocolate too,
Biscuit and wafer,
Toffees and chew!

Soft centres and caramel,
There's nutty ones too,
I love chocolate so much,
I don't think I can share it with you!

Chocolate, chocolate,
It tastes so good,
Chocolate, chocolate,
It's ideal for your pud!

Amy Jimenez (12)
Convent Of Jesus & Mary Language College

City Life Poem

I see the cars go by night after night,
I watch the pigeons take flight.
Rubbish on the floor, gum on the ground,
The busy people walking around.
I see the pollution destroying the Earth,
I don't see people planting in turf.
I want to see flowers,
But there are millions of towers.

Zoe Ryan (12)
Convent Of Jesus & Mary Language College

Seasons!

Winter, winter,
You are so cold,
You make us shiver,
Especially for those who are bold,
You also bring us snow from which
We can build snowmen.

Spring, spring,
You spring back with flowers
And fresh grass that we can roll in
And also with some mild showers,
Daffodils, roses and daisies are my favourite.

Summer, summer,
What fun, you can finally go to the seaside,
Bathe in the water and make some sandcastles,
It's not dark in the summer,
So you can stay out late and enjoy yourself.

Autumn, autumn,
Oh what joy,
Leaves start to fall
And a rainbow of colours,
Yellow, orange, crimson and gold.

Oh what fun,
For all of these are our
Seasons!

Severina Trifonova (12)
Convent Of Jesus & Mary Language College

Treasured Friend

I lost a treasured friend today
The little dog who used to lay
Her gentle head upon my knee
And shared her silent thoughts with me
She'll come no longer to my call
Retrieve no more her favourite ball
A voice far greater than my own
Has called her to his golden throne

Although my eyes are filled with tears
I thank him for the happy years
He let her spend down here with me
And for her love and loyalty
When it is time for me to go
And join her there, this much I know
I shall not fear the transient dark
For she will greet me with her bark.

Jade Jeeves (13)
Convent Of Jesus & Mary Language College

Life In The City!

Oh what a gloomy day,
But then again it's a normal day for the streets of London,
Cars go by,
Cars come by,
The sound of children's laughter
And crying rings through my ears,
Busy-bodies run through the streets, late for work,
Schoolgirls and boys roam the streets,
Without a care in the world about how late they are for school.
Blowing of horns, echoing of distressed voices,
It's a normal day for the streets of London.

Aisling McDonagh (12)
Convent Of Jesus & Mary Language College

If I Was . . .

If I was a queen;
    I would be mean.
If I was a cat;
    I'd play on the green.
If I was a model;
    I'd wear purple.
If I was a snail;
    I'd like to growl.
If I was an owl;
    I'd like to howl.
If I was a moon;
    I'd like a sun.
If I was a boy;
    I'd be able to run.

But I'm just me, so I'm happy to be.

Tamara Smith (12)
Convent Of Jesus & Mary Language College

Books

Books are great fun,
Made to entertain, scare and stun,
Just open one up
And take a look,
There's nothing like an enjoyable book,
I like the romantic ones, full of love,
I like the scary ones, about aliens from above,
I like the funny ones, they make me giggle,
You get books in all different sizes, big and little,
TV is good but books are great,
Never to read one again, I'd hate!

Sophia Mackay (12)
Convent Of Jesus & Mary Language College

Where Is The Love?

Where is the place that people can rest
Where angels sing and songbirds nest?
A place where people judge others and put them to shame,
Shouldn't we all be equal and treated the same?
Look me in the eye and tell me the truth,
We do not hold love, God's got the proof,
If we can stop war, fighting and death,
We would all be better and be rid of this mess,
If we can be friends and stay loyal again,
We shouldn't be enemies but stand up for all men.
When I look out my window to heal all my scars,
Stars are staring, they are shining by Mars,
Cos I know the truth at least my own,
I shall not argue nor shall I moan,
If you can join me at least to spread peace,
I'll share all my riches . . . well a hundred at least!

Nicole Barton (13)
Convent Of Jesus & Mary Language College

Cats

Cats are big, cats are small,
Cats are short, cats are tall,
I love cats,
They love me,
We're a happy family.

I have a sister, I have a mother,
I have a father,
But I don't have a brother.
We love our cats, so should you,
They slink around all night and day,
We don't know what they do.

Claire Johnston (11)
Convent Of Jesus & Mary Language College

Vanished . . .

She sulked around every day looking for a friend,
But no one had a heart for her, they put her to the end.
She never did one thing wrong, she was a perfect child,
But because of school she ended that and made herself go wild.
She trashed her house, she trashed the school, she trashed
                                  everything in sight,
But her poor heart wasn't filled with rage, it was filled with fright.
The fright was due to selfishness because of the people there,
One day they beat her, hit her, punched her and dragged
                                    her by her hair.
They dragged her to the top of the school, where the roof
                                  was black and sloppy,
Then they beat her more and more until she was as red as a poppy.
They pushed her off until she fell, the building was quite high,
She fell and fell, down and down, they wanted her to die.
After she was dead and gone, no one cared a bit;
The bullies dumped the body away after she was severely hit.
When I look at her gravestone now that six months have gone,
I know the ungrateful bullies had got their way and won.
They didn't give a thought for me, although I am the mother,
But deep down they know for sure I haven't got another.
They did the same to my husband too, just for pure fun;
They stabbed him out on the road when he was walking with his son.
They laugh, they play, they live now, although they know
                                  she was banished,
But because no people cared for her, they just think she . . . vanished.

Joshna Fernando (11)
Convent Of Jesus & Mary Language College

My Passionate Love

Deep in my heart and soul, lives a love,
A love I set my desire on expressing,
The eagerness to be loved by someone as handsome as him,
The position in which his eyes lay,
When he smiles or puts on a serious look,
Oh it makes my heart leap twice,
As the greedy intention to be loved by him patrols the
veins in my blood.
I know he's the one I am destined to be with,
I can just vaguely remember this piece of puzzle that was
once complete.
The picture of me and him in an embrace, kissing passionately
near the lakes,

The harmonising music that filled our ears,
The angles and cherubs that encircled us,
Butterflies flying around our heads
And the sun setting near our hearts,
Joining us together as man and wife.
But now as I sit and write, I weep in sadness,
As our love was killed by intense hate and evil,
Like a stab in the heart with a knife,
The distraught and destruction caused,
Made us lose contact and fall apart,
Our endless love that was Heaven-bound died,
So now we seek desperately for each other on the grounds of Earth.

Sophia Bosah (13)
Convent Of Jesus & Mary Language College

A Poem About Bullying

Despicable ganging up against vulnerable prey,
The bully safe within his protective bubble,
The victim never having his say
And on its way, ready to start, is trouble.

Weaponry, even just boots,
Can find its mark and hurt
And nobody cares two hoots,
Because you're just a squirt.

All on your own, no friends to tell,
That you don't know what to do;
It's as if you're trapped in a dark well,
You tremble at the slightest *boo!*

You're broken down to pondering,
What will happen next
And while you're still wondering
Your tormentors come and fulfil the text.

Finally you're just held together by the thought
'It has to end soon', even though you cannot see,
When that thought that you have sought,
Will come to release you from that hive of bees.

Then you crack and all is told,
Justice dealt out and your troubles ended,
But this whole tragedy might get a second hold
And then who knows how the problems will be fended.

Joanna Maguire (12)
Convent Of Jesus & Mary Language College

The Door Shut Tightly

It was the crack of dawn
And the door was shut tightly.

> Poor old Jane, hated air,
> Her windows and her doors were kept locked,
> Four hours later, Jane collapses
> And dies with no air suction.

15 years later the Wilsons move in,
They always seem to be locked out,
But it is known Jane's back home.
She hates the company, she says
With a deep breath, with no sound

> The Wilsons keep the door open
> But the door shut tightly.

A gasp of air, with a whisper
Screams 'Open the door now'
But the door shut tightly.

> It was the crack of dawn, then
> The door opened, with a flash of light,
> Jane struggles for air.

But once again, the door shut tightly.

> The Wilsons open the door,
> But for Jane the door shut tightly.

Jane bangs on the door, she tries to get out,
But at the crack of dawn, no one about.

> But the door shut tightly,
> With a deep breath, with no sound.

Nicole Moses (14)
Convent Of Jesus & Mary Language College

The Countryside

There are so many flowers
It never ever showers

The sun is always shining
There are never people sighing

The birds sing
Oh! There are so many lovely things

There are lovely smells
And you can hear the church bells

The horses are galloping
While the dogs are paddling

The stars' bright light
Can cause shadows to give you a fright

The owls go tu-whit tu-whoo
While the cows go moo

The rooster goes cock-a-doodle-doo
And that's what happens in the countryside.

Sally Da Silva (11)
Convent Of Jesus & Mary Language College

Roses Are . . .

Roses are as red as raw blood,
Roses are as beautiful as your true love,
Roses are as gracious as butterflies,
Roses are precious, just like you,
Roses are as spectacular as a play,
Roses are there to declare my love for you.

Racheal Canney (13)
Convent Of Jesus & Mary Language College

Poem

I remember, I remember,
The house where I was born,
The little window where the sun
Came peeping in at morn;
He never came a wink too soon,
Nor brought too long a day,
But now, I often wish the night
Had borne my breath away.

I remember, I remember,
The rose, red and white;
The violets and the lily-cups,
Those flowers made of light!
The lilacs where the robin built
And where my brother set
The laburnum on his birthday –
The tree is living yet!

I remember, I remember,
Where I used to swing;
And thought the air must rush as fresh
To swallows on the wing:
My spirit flew in feathers than,
That is so heavy now
And summer pools could hardly cool
The fever on my brow!

Marina Fakhouri (12)
Convent Of Jesus & Mary Language College

The Funfair

I love the funfair,
It's bubbly, bright and fun,
There are so many things to do there,
You can eat lots of candyfloss, even a ton.

All the lights glow at night
And all the other super things,
Some of the rides are at an extending height,
It would make you feel like you have wings.

There are lots of fun rides,
Some that go high, low and round
And some that go from side to side,
I love it when the fair comes to my town.

Now that I have been on all the rides,
I can see it's getting dark,
I've laughed so much I think I've split my sides,
The funfair has certainly left on me its joyous mark.

Pauline Fallon (12)
Convent Of Jesus & Mary Language College

Jewellery

J is for jewels in lots of colours
E is for emerald one of the jewels
W is for watch, a piece of jewellery
E is for an elegant item
L is for lucky charm bracelet
L is for a luxury item
E is for earrings that always sparkle
R is for ruby another jewel
Y is for young to old, the ages that buy it.

Sinead Daly (12)
Convent Of Jesus & Mary Language College

The Clockwork Monster!

He wades through the town
Cracking the pavements and
Scorching the bricks as he passes,
Behind follows darkness
And darkness alone.

He is the keeper of darkness,
He is the master of the hands under your beds,
He is the clockwork monster
And the clockwork monster alone.

It is he who gives the sun the sign for 'lights out',
He gives the moon its eerie silver glow
And it is he who breathes his icy cold breath for wind,
He controls the shadow man hiding behind your door!
He is the clockwork monster
And the clockwork monster alone!

Aniah Boakye-Smith (11)
Convent Of Jesus & Mary Language College

Justin Timberlake

Gorgeous in every way,
From night to the break of day.
Talented is his gift,
Given to him from up above.

He is an influence on me,
That's why I love him especially.
Justin, I don't know what to do,
Just sit here and listen to you.

Singing, singing, singing away,
That's why I love you in a special way.

Anisha Allen (12)
Convent Of Jesus & Mary Language College

Music

Music can be fast,
Music can be slow,
I love music even if it's low,
Jazz, rock, even pop,
I love music but then it stops.

The birds stopped singing,
The children stopped laughing,
Tears start to fall
And the air is filled with war,
So many things have stopped,
But why, where, when did the music stop?

But then someone laughing,
Who could be laughing
Where there's no dancing?

The little boy who was laughing proud,
The young boy who turned off the sound,
No love, no share, not even a care,
The little boy who turned off the sound.

Olivia Serwa Bonsu (11)
Convent Of Jesus & Mary Language College

My Poem

R eckless and loud
A mazing in the crowds
C aring and sweet
H appy when the robins go tweet, tweet, tweet
E nergetic and alive
L ovin' it when my dad drives
L ovely and kind
E asy on a Sunday morning.

Rachelle Awoyemi (11)
Convent Of Jesus & Mary Language College

Ballet

I do ballet
And here's what I have to say
Point your toes
Keep your head high
And off she goes
And don't be shy
If you practice hard
Bring your belt
And your leotard
You will have felt
Happy and not sad
You are very good
So don't be mad
I'm sure you would
Stand out from the crowd
You're superior from the rest
So do me proud
Because you are the best.

Kimberley Joseph-Williams (11)
Convent Of Jesus & Mary Language College

Bright Light

One night
I saw this light
Coming from the sky
Which caught my eye
It was so bright
It looked so right
So I told my friend, Kate
My trusty mate
About the night
I saw the bright light.

Theresa Currie (13)
Convent Of Jesus & Mary Language College

All About Me

Rachael Rubio is my name
I'm really good at reading
I like snuggling up with a book
Especially in bed, before I'm sleeping

I hang around Victoria
She puts on airs and graces
She's now my good friend
And I'm always seeing new faces

I'm a person who likes hair-dos
Also Gini Rabbit and Hello Kitty
I certainly don't like bad hair days
That's when I start to feel guilty

It's now time to say goodbye to you
I hope you enjoyed reading this
I also like to do art
You are now on the good reader's list!

Rachael Rubio (11)
Convent Of Jesus & Mary Language College

Friendship

To be a friend is to be:
Loyal and caring,
Look out for your friend,
Be loving and sharing,
Make sure you're supportive,
You respect and trust
And being there when needed
Is always a must.

Grace Coakley (14)
Convent Of Jesus & Mary Language College

My Life

My life is so wonderful,
You can't imagine,
Every day I have a huge
Surprise in my heart.

My mum and dad always
Make surprises for me on special times,
Also when I do something special for them,
They always give me wonderful gifts.

I don't have any brothers or sisters,
Sometimes I feel lonely,
But I've got birds called
Michael and Cute.

One thing I needed to say,
When I'm older, I wish to be a singer or an actress.

Vania Ferreira De Jesus (12)
Convent Of Jesus & Mary Language College

Granny

Now we lay you down to rest,
Your face as white as snow.
We know where you are is the best,
But still, we have sorrow.

I didn't know you very well,
Only saw you on holidays,
I remember when you used to tell
Me what to do and say.

But now you have gone far away
And we are all left here,
I really wish that you could stay,
Though I still feel you near.

Sophie Manning (12)
Convent Of Jesus & Mary Language College

Flowers

Flowers ease my troubled mind when I am feeling sad
Their scent blows in my open window making me feel glad
I love to see the burst of colours early in the spring
They brighten up my world with the pleasures that they bring
The pearly trees of snowdrops are first to show their heads
The daffodils and narcissi are sleeping in their beds
The sweetly scented hyacinths tell me that winter's passed
The cherry blossom in the trees say spring's approaching fast
In summer the bees are busy collecting pollen for the hive
And the blood-red sunset makes you glad that you're alive
The insects visit many flowers and pollination brings
And makes me marvel at God's almighty scheme of things
Autumn takes the flowers away with the cold October chill
And leaves the Earth a starker place; but it is God's will
Winter makes us realise all life has its time too
But spring tells us it's everlasting, shining and brand new.

Rachel Harris (11)
Convent Of Jesus & Mary Language College

Not Me

Every girl would like to be the fairy on the Christmas tree
Not me
I would rather be into kung-fu and fight against Bruce Lee

Every little girl would like to be the queen of May and reign for a day
Not me
I would rather stow away and hitch-hike across the USA

Every girl would like to be a bridesmaid or a bride
Not me
I would rather ride a motorbike or hide inside a cave
Or save a penalty shot at Wembley or fly a shuttle into space!

I know what other girls would like to be!
Not me.

Tracey Atallah (11)
Convent Of Jesus & Mary Language College

It's All About The Music

There's the pop, the rap and the hip-hop,
The R 'n' B, the classical and the rock,
The groupies, the band and the lead singers,
Ballerinas, tap dancers and the swingers.

The head-banging music and the mosh pit,
TOTP and a number one hit,
Good Charlotte, Britney and Destiny's Child,
From pink princess to seriously wild.

Instrumental lessons and choir too,
Gospel, jazz and the blues.
Lisa Simpson plays the saxophone,
I play an instrument of my own.

I have a flute lesson once a week,
The music I play is rather bleak.
With most singing comes a dance,
Also known as a prance.

The dances I did were ballet and tap,
Not just to classical, but also rap.
My favourite instrument is the drum,
But I'd prefer to sing or even hum.

Emma Dubrey (12)
Convent Of Jesus & Mary Language College

Music

Music, music all around
Music, music, listen to the sound!
Music lively, music slow
Music makes your body go, go!

Joyful, tearful, happy and sad
Everyone is music mad!
Music different, different kinds
Music is always on my mind!

Nicola Wall (12)
Convent Of Jesus & Mary Language College

Opposite

When you cross my line
I won't mind
When you hate me
I will love you back
When you insult me, I will do nothing
I will just stand and watch
When you spread rumours about me
I will just listen
When you beat me up
I will let you
But when you say that
I am not good at anything
And I am useless
I will flip . . .
When you cross my line
I will cross your line
When you hate me
I will hate you back
When you insult me
I will insult you
When you beat me up
I will beat you up
When you spread rumours about me
I will spread rumours about you.

Mercy-Linda Sarkodie Frempong (13)
Convent Of Jesus & Mary Language College

Sunset

As the sun sets,
The soft breeze swifts along the palm trees,
The water trickles against the golden sand,
Beaming into the sunlight,
The sun starts to set into the dark blue sea,
As the sky turns black and the stars are twinkling,
In the sunset sea.

Ofome Simei-Akajagbo (11)
Convent Of Jesus & Mary Language College

The Fish In The Bowl

The fish in the bowl said to himself
'This fish bowl will not improve my health,
It hasn't been changed, it hasn't been cleaned,
It's full of dirt it now seems,
I'll never have a clean bowl.
I'll never get to fulfil my role,
To warn all fish to not come to this house,
It's safer to be eaten instead of a mouse,
By the cat who loves to eat fish
And get eaten not even on a dish,
But on the cold, hard floor
And get killed while you're very sore,
From being clawed by the cat's sharp claws
And being touched by the cat's muddy paws,
Oh woe, oh woe, oh woe to be,
I'm going to end not happily,
But suffocated by all the dirt
And end up being very hurt.'
Then the fish died
And no one cried.

Kerrie Daly (12)
Convent Of Jesus & Mary Language College

School

Mum, do I have to go to school today?
Come on, Mum, it's the middle of May
The children at school are so bad
Mum, they make me sad

Of course you have to go to school today
Even though it's the middle of May
So get into your 4-seater
Remember, you're the head teacher!

Michelle Kwashie (11)
Convent Of Jesus & Mary Language College

Only Here For The Ride!

He walked the road with no care
He scurried through alleys and cracks
You could see the fleas in his hair
All he got were bangs and whacks

He scuttled through sewers and pipes
He was rancid and ragged and sick
He thought over his worries and gripes
And the clouds above him were thick

His road was beset with trouble
Staying alive was his biggest worry
His world was a mountain of rubble
What's the point to all this, what's the hurry?

He begged on the streets with no shame
He lost all his dignity and pride
To the people that passed he had no name
He was only here for the ride!

Amelia Bhasin (12)
Convent Of Jesus & Mary Language College

The Sea

The sea is a place filled with happiness
It's very blue and big
The thing I always have to worry is that
Jellyfish sting

The sea is filled with seagulls that always sing
They are sometimes little pests
The thing I always have to worry is that
They might peck me on the head

The sea is great and cold
I love swimming in it
Now the thing I have to worry about is that
I have to go to bed!

Anastasiya Tymchyshyn (11)
Convent Of Jesus & Mary Language College

Love Virus

Love is like a poison coursing through your veins.
Infecting every part of you:
        Controlling you
        Taking you prisoner.

No one is immune to love, anyone can catch it.
It can strike at any time:
        With anyone
        At any place.

Although it takes a while to kick in,
When it does, you'll know. You can't sleep
        Eat
        Breathe.

To receive this virus in return is fatal,
Not to is deadly . . .

Theresa Omisore (14)
Convent Of Jesus & Mary Language College

Year 8!

Had a break which was great,
Back again now in Year 8.

Year 7 was quite a big challenge,
But I got through it and I managed.

Will try my best to work hard all year through
And to show my teachers what I can do.

I've made so many friends which includes teachers too,
That I cannot name all to you.

I hope my education continues to be successful
During my time in the Convent of Jesus and Mary.

Katie Bergin (12)
Convent Of Jesus & Mary Language College

The Usual Mushy Stuff

You always know the right things to say
Just open your mouth and I'm happy
Your voice, such a huge comfort to me
I like you . . . no, I love you! Can't you see?

I'm a wuss when it comes to feelings
Hiding them from you and myself
I'll probably never let you know
I'm shy, I'll never let my love show

You're as important as the fresh air
As needed as the food I've to eat
Your sense of humour as vital as fun
God only knows how much I need you, Hun

You always seem so distant although
You may be standing right next to me
I long to hold your body warmly
I must send an obvious sign surely.

Katrina Powell (14)
Convent Of Jesus & Mary Language College

Shine . . .

The sun shines down so bright
My eyes are blinded by the light
When the moon hits the night
Your eyes sparkle upon the night
When you sing me to sleep
I'll fall and drift away
To somewhere you'll love and stay
I'll love you and you love me
We'll be together and maybe as three.

Christina Fahy (12)
Convent Of Jesus & Mary Language College

Life As A Teen

So much hurting
And so much pain
I feel so badly
When I'm alone

The way I run
And the way I hide
Makes me so ashamed
When I remember back

I don't feel loved
By any human alive
And admitting this
Is the worst part of the ride

Getting on with life
And forgetting the past
It's much too difficult
For a girl my age.

Damilola Soile (14)
Convent Of Jesus & Mary Language College

Things I Really Appreciate In Life!

Things I really appreciate in life are
The birds and the bees,
The leaves on the trees,
The sea and the sand,
The grass on the land,
The butter and bread,
The hair on my head,
The shoes on my feet,
The people I meet,
The clouds in the sky,
When I say goodbye.

Jodie Lawes (12)
Convent Of Jesus & Mary Language College

The Two Faces Of Love

I told you you'd never have a reason to doubt
I am something you'll never go without.
I cannot stand us being apart,
You will always be in my heart.

I saw something new in your eyes,
They were intriguing and alive.
A flame burning behind those lids,
A fire to set me alight.

Something doused the fire.

All alone I wait, calling,
No longer sunny, the rain is falling,
Because of love I'm slowly dying,
Inside my heart, I'm weeping, crying.

I gave you all of me
And now I don't know what to do,
Like a fool I let myself become
Totally in love with you.

I've seen the faces of love,
I gave you my love in vain,
At first I felt such pleasure,
Now I feel the pain.

Kemi Banjoko (14)
Convent Of Jesus & Mary Language College

Love

A chemical reaction,
Causing us to change,
Making us regret our choice,
If they don't feel the same.

To concentrate is hard,
It makes you lose your mind,
Eating, sleeping is all gone,
Your soulmate's hard to find.

Lana Guascone (15)
Convent Of Jesus & Mary Language College

Love Is . . .

Love is the smell of roses
In the morning,
It is the sight of the sun
As the day is dawning.

Love is an over joyous
Flow of emotions,
The feeling you get
When full of devotion.

Love fills you like a
Crescendo of feelings,
All with valuable,
Sentimental meanings.

Love is a force,
That can fill you with hope,
Even with the deepest wounds,
It can help you cope.

Natasha Bannister (15)
Convent Of Jesus & Mary Language College

Love That Kills

The thorn in my side
Belongs to the rose
That is you, my love
The bittersweet scent that chokes me

The tears in my eyes
Belong to the pain
That is you, my love
The piece of glass that cuts me

Please, hold my heart and break it.

Katie Johnston (14)
Convent Of Jesus & Mary Language College

Friends

Friends are like family but you get to pick and choose
You're not forced to be with them so you can never lose

Perfect friends are really hard to find
They should be caring, thoughtful, loving and kind

They shouldn't tease but they should really care
They should be gentle, sweet, forgiving and fair

A good friend will ignore your really large zit
If you think you're fat, they'll help you get fit

They should be the people with which you can joke
Not the ones who just hang around, drink, swear and smoke

If you ever happen to have a little fall out
They'll try to make up with you – no doubt

A friend always listens to what you have to say
You love to talk to them at any time of the day

Just remember good friends are hard to come by
So treat them right and never tell them a lie

Once you have found some, never let them go
They are great friends and you should let them know.

Tabitha Skinner (14)
Convent Of Jesus & Mary Language College

Poem On Love – That 4 Letter Word

The 4 letter word that when being with you can be felt
The 4 letter word that makes your heart melt
The 4 letter word that sets your mind on high
The 4 letter word that always makes you cry
It only takes 4 letters, so don't hide your love away
It only takes 4 letters, so give your love today.

Theresa Lisk (15)
Convent Of Jesus & Mary Language College

Truth Of The Heart

The moment I saw you, I knew you were mine,
My destiny, my one true love
And without you in my life I am surrounded in darkness,
You are the light which shines within,
Your love keeps me alive.

The first time you kissed me, you took my soul from my body
through my lips,
My heart belongs to you alone,
You keep me safe, where no harm can come to me
And without you in my life I am lonely,
Surely loneliness has to be wrong when a love such as this exists?

The first time we made love, I knew what I felt for you could never end,
I know there will never be anything stronger than what I
feel for you now,
The passion, the embrace, I find you irresistible
And no one could ever love or care for you more than I
And no one ever will, for our love is like a candle that will forever burn.

I truly believe I was born to love you,
This feeling will never end,
I will always love you.

Sarah Libberton (14)
Convent Of Jesus & Mary Language College

My Garden Of Eden

A tree for every tear I shed for you
A tree for all the laughter we used to have
A tree for every kiss I gave you
A tree for every tragedy we've got through
A tree for the love we had
And a forest burning for the knowledge in my heart.

Catia Carvalho (14)
Convent Of Jesus & Mary Language College

Secret Feelings

I need to get over you, I really know I should
But here I am drowning in tears like I never thought I would.
Here I am constantly thinking of you,
Why must you hurt me the way you do?
In your arms is where I want to be,
I'm falling in love with you, why can't you see?
I know you don't feel for me, just tell me why,
Because how can you expect me to just pass you by?
I'm wanting you here almost all the time,
Because when you're here it feels so fine.
I want to stop loving you, but it feels so right,
Just give us a chance to talk properly - no one else in sight.
I need to get over you, I really know I should
But I'm glad I didn't because now I've got you -
I always thought I could!

Amandla Crichlow (14)
Convent Of Jesus & Mary Language College

Love

Tender, lingering, soft touch,
What is this feeling I admire so much?
Grabbing, pulling, tearing apart,
Who can mend my breaking heart?

I need to feel whole, complete,
I'd like to be courteous to people I meet.
With this thing missing, I cannot go on,
Before I can catch it, it will be gone.

I've found my muse,
But I'm still so confused.
It's love I've found,
Shackles go, I'm unbound.

Shikisha Richards (14)
Convent Of Jesus & Mary Language College

Love Hurts

It was midnight, the moon out and the stars shining bright,
Waiting in the darkness,
I longed for his touch,
His reassuring gaze,
The smoothness of his lips,
The subtleness of his voice whispering into my ear,
Penetrating into my heart,
Causing me to tingle and make me feel loved.

My heart pounding like a lion creeping up on its prey,
My lungs yearning for air during a hot summer day,
Wondering if my love will come, would he dare show his face?
In front of the Capulet's race!
'Romeo, Romeo! Wherefore art thou Romeo?'
Time has fast been spent,
No sign of the one, my heart awaits,
Another day will come and go,
But as for seeing my love,
Who knows?

Anita Asante (14)
Convent Of Jesus & Mary Language College

My Poem

If kisses were trees,
I would give you a forest.

If hugs were water,
I would give you a sea.

But if you ever need love,
You always have me!

Katya Lourenco (11)
Convent Of Jesus & Mary Language College

The Exam

As the examinee takes the floor,
The judges stare with adore.

The music starts to play,
So she has to start straight away.

Watch her as she swishes and sways,
Listen while the music plays.

Kicking, jumping and twirls and splits,
Judges mark numbers and ticks.

Finally it was time for the finishing pose,
As she walked out, the judges rose.

Teachers and pupils saying well done,
But to her the worrying has just begun.

Jennifer Payne-McDonald (12)
Convent Of Jesus & Mary Language College

Why?

Why are you hurting me?
I thought you were meant to be,
You made me cry,
Now I feel like I need to die.
When I turn the corner, you're there,
Inside I feel so bare.

I feel so low,
Even though,
I hate you so.

At night I cry,
Because one night I prayed,
That one day you could have been mine.

Alex Gregory (12)
Convent Of Jesus & Mary Language College

We Were Meant To Meet Long Ago

As our eyes meet
There is love in the air
Yet we look away
An element of romance is there.

We meet again
But how can I know how you feel?
Constantly thinking about you
You appear distant and surreal.

I don't know whether to love or hate
I feel constant uncertainty
Our eyes meet once again
And I know this love will never cease to be.

Hold me in your arms
Never let me go
I'm only half a person without you
Cupid's arrow has hit me
We were meant to meet long ago.

Francesca Hendra (14)
Convent Of Jesus & Mary Language College

Tammy Rocks!

T ammy is the best shop!
A nd you can get fab tops!
M ini skirts you can get anywhere!
M ini skirts are the best if you get them there!
Y ou know where to shop when you're going out
and they sell good make-up for a glossy pout!

Jennifer Rodriguez (11)
Convent Of Jesus & Mary Language College

I Thought You Loved Me

I thought you loved me
But that wasn't true
I don't know
If I can get over you

I saw all those girls
You treated me like dirt
Even though you knew
Just how much I would hurt

I still look for you
Outside my front door
Still dreaming of you
For evermore

I thought you loved me
But that wasn't true
I think you know
That I still love you.

Francesca Naylor (14)
Convent Of Jesus & Mary Language College

Feelings

Feelings can be good, feelings can be bad,
Feelings can be happy, feelings can be sad,
Everyone has feelings deep in their soul,
Everyone has feelings that they don't show,
Fear is a feeling, anger is too,
Feelings control the things we do,
Rumours hurt your feelings, lies do too,
So remember everyone has feelings just like you.

Ellen Morrissey (13)
Convent Of Jesus & Mary Language College

Haterz

They synchronise
To tell lies
Do not hate me
Because I am me
Do not envy
Because I am free
Capable of greatness
Trust me
We are living in trial and tribulation
The negative light
We need to build a new nation
Don't need to pass war stations
Where scheming eyes
Have no patience
Do not hesitate
Just relate
To the words of wisdom
Passion of love
They have synchronised
Pow, pow, pow
Forget the lies . . .

Laura Martell (15)
Convent Of Jesus & Mary Language College

Music

M usic is magical and fun.
U sing assorted instruments.
S pecial to me, it's number one.
I magination goes wild.
C reativity is a talent for some!

Kelly Clarke (11)
Convent Of Jesus & Mary Language College

Passion

He loves her with a passion,
She hates him with a passion.
But what is passion truly?
Is it a feeling, a sentiment, an emotion?
Is it an unrequited longing or desire?
Passion lives within us all,
It lies there sleeping, waiting, begging us to work its will,
Passion takes us over, takes over our senses forcing us to listen.
We are left with no other choice but to,
Passion is dangerous,
It weakens us,
Makes us vulnerable,
Hurts us.
We sometimes think that life without passion would grant us peace,
But what would we be without passion?
We would be empty
And life would be cold
And so she loves him with a passion
And he hates her with a passion
And they both live and breathe in spite and because of it.

Melissa Santos (14)
Convent Of Jesus & Mary Language College

My Idol, Pharell Williams

P harell Williams is the finest man alive
H ave always liked him ever since I was five
A nybody who says he can't sing is crazy
R ather than hearing him, I prefer seeing him, it just phases me
E ven though a lot of people don't like him, I think he's lovely
L ovelier than Raz-B
L uckily he's there for me.

Fordos Michael (12)
Convent Of Jesus & Mary Language College

A Love Poem

Oh my love if wishes come true
Then I'd have to say my wish is you
Never have I felt this way
All my morals I betray
Just to think of you, a sweet thought
That goes against what I was taught
Just knowing you are right there
Is getting hard for me to bear
Seeing your beautiful face
Makes my heart race
And I know for sure what I feel
Is not fake but truly real

Dreams can come true
I know this because of you
This heart of mine sings your name
And I know I'll never be the same
You've cast me under your love spell
One you cast oh so very well
By the way you smile, laugh and talk
And the cute little way you walk
I'm afraid I've become addicted to you
And every small thing you do
So to you I give my heart
And pray to God we never part

My dear love I'm in love with you
I hope you feel the same way too.

Helen Miller (14)
Convent Of Jesus & Mary Language College

My Mum And Dad

My mum is great, she's so much fun,
She's just had a baby,
My brother, her son.

My dad is funny, I've always loved him,
He's always telling jokes,
I really love him, he's not at all dim.

Gemma Goode (11)
Convent Of Jesus & Mary Language College

Swimming Limerick

It happened one day at Grove Park School
A girl fell in the swimming pool
She fell for someone
And she saw the sun
She had fun, she thought it was cool.

Bijal Vadher (17)
Grove Park School

Firework Night

Every firework night people like going outside,
They like to light them up,
It goes up in the sky,
Whee . . . *bang!*
And it makes the sky pretty and bright,
The whole night.

Neda Khosravi (12)
Grove Park School

Young Love

Together forever we shall stay,
Letting our love grow stronger, day by day.
Wishes made upon the stars in the sky,
Knowing this love will never die.

Hope and dream this love is for real,
Knowing what's going on, knowing how we feel.
Showing our love and showing we care,
No longer playing a silly game of truth or dare.

Being here for one another
And showing love for each other,
I'm going to be only your girl
And this is because you have changed my world.

You have put trust in me like no one else will,
You loved me then and you love me still.
I believe in this world everyone has a soulmate,
I also believe we met not only through fate.

But we met because we are meant to be
And that's what I'm trying to make you see.
You and I must work through this relationship together
And when we go through the worst, we will make it better.

So from here on out it's just me and you
And for that – I love only you.

Saima Hamed (15)
Grove Park School

Chameleon

I stand
Ever still
People watch me
Never see me
I am a chameleon
Always there
Not seen
Part of the furniture
Part of the scenery
I just fade away
Melt into the background
Dissolve into the crowd
How I fear being noticed
Yet long to be in focus
I just play my part
I just do my job
Doing everything to the letter
Perfectly done
No cause for complaint
Never a reason to be given a second glance
People's eyes just glaze over me
Never see I'm there
Sometimes I just want to jump up and scream
Force them to realise I exist
Of course I don't
I never do
I go on
Just as before
Ride on, on an endless wheel
A never changing
Never-ending turn of invisible events.

Bryony Chapman-Allan (13)
Highgate Wood School

Johnny

As I looked from a blink,
I could not think,
My stiff neck froze into one place.
All I could see was a pale face,
Lying on the hospital bed as pale as snow.

I awkwardly moved my neck around,
Looking for something else to see,
But all I could see was the repetitive picture
Of his still body in my mind.
Helplessly crying a silent cry for help.

Through the blurry tears filling up in my eyes,
Like fog on a winter's night,
I watched the person that loved him the most,
Banging his head on the smooth wall,
Building up tears in his eyes,
Forcing themselves not to come out,
But I knew they would burst any second,
Like a pipe shooting out water.

He was so young,
Yet so innocent.
Now he's gone,
But he will always be living gold in my memories.

Amna Malik (12)
Hornsey School For Girls

Too Late

As I killed him, I knew what was going to happen to me,
I thought I was going to a dark, scary place.
Instead I'm lying here listening to all the people talking,
Sounding like bees whizzing around,
Instead I'm lying here smelling all the nicest and sweetest
                                        smells of sweets,
Although I can't eat them.
Instead I'm lying here feeling my boneless back,
As boneless as a invertebrate.
Instead I'm lying here looking at the tiniest cracks on the floor
                                        I've ever seen,
Instead I'm thinking, why am I here,
Lying in an old bed, being looked after?
I remember, I'm a hero, I saved children from the hot, red flames,
I've got something to be proud of,
It's too late now, it's too late.

Prinal Patel (13)
Hornsey School For Girls

An Apology

I can't believe I hit him,
The sound of his body crashing against the door.
All I could see was the image of him running out of the door.
He looked like a cat running out into the night.
I could hear the echo of his voice saying, 'You don't yell at him.'
He sounded like the wind passing by.
I wonder where he has run away to, is he safe?
Is he hungry or cold like ice?
I can feel his long greasy hair,
Softly sliding through my fingers like soft silk.
I could feel the palm of my hand sweating,
It was as hot as fire.
As I sat there thinking about him,
I could taste the bitterness of my tongue.
I wonder where he is and will he come back to his sweet home?

Sheila Tagoe (12)
Hornsey School For Girls

Whisper

I hear the sounds of the rushing stream
Loud and soft like crushing thunder
And a quiet, sweet voice as honey
Whispering against me.

The rising of the shining sun
Like gold which I've wished for
And now is done.

Life was not as sweet as honey
And neither was it good to be
Poor without no money.

I felt a cool breeze and all the handsome
Friends I need.

At visualising point it's as
Wonderful as silver heaven's
Imagination.

The finest golden wheat field
So gold and cream with the
Smell of sweet lavender gently
Blowing against me.

The singing bird and a bright new life
But now I'm nearly finished and my time
Has come for me to go.
I'm going somewhere else which is bright
Like paradise where I'll stay forever, till the end of time.

Aayesha Hamidu (12)
Hornsey School For Girls

The Sunset

People busily rushing by, nobody seems to notice me,
The darkness surrounding me, seems like a thick blanket
                                    suffocating me.
It feels like I'm a lost child looking for my mother.

I can't reach out and touch anything, only my body,
The tips of my fingers, as cold as ice,
Like I'm in a raging river of hate.

I can only hear screams,
It's like a constant nightmare never-ending.
Like I'm in a time warp stuck there alone,
Nobody to talk to,
Nobody to shout at,
Someone please help me.

Then, then I remember the sunset,
The good times before I got hurt,
The times that I cherish with my friends,
The times that I thought would never end.

I was wrong . . .

Taneka Morris-Forbes (13)
Hornsey School For Girls

True Wealth?

There is a question - what is true wealth?
Is it money or is it good health?
Is it flashy cars and winning the lottery
Or is it love and family?

People say it is a long holiday in an expensive hotel,
But don't you need a loved one to share it as well?
Others say it is big houses and expensive things,
But isn't a mother more precious than diamonds and rings?

I think that love is more precious than a new dress
And that friendship is more important than worrying about having less
And patience is always a good virtue,
Which is better than having something beautiful or new
And maybe a nice car is worthless compared to kindness and respect
And not having any money is nothing compared to neglect.

There is a question - what is true wealth?
It is not money but it is good health,
Because in the whole world, all of the money
Cannot replace love, respect and family.

Natasha Shotunde (13)
Hornsey School For Girls

Love

As he laid his head down to sleep
I ran, I ran, I ran to weep
I ran to a shop about to get robbed
I stood there feeling my heart beat
I felt the blood pumping through my veins
I could smell him just like yesterday
If he was alive just one more day
I would fulfil his wishes

I loved him you know
Why did he have to go?
Not him, he wasn't ready
Why? Why? Why?
Why did he have to go in those burning flames?
I could have stopped him
The flames, the red, the orange and the yellow
The orange and the yellow just like the sunset
The red just like the blood that comes out of you and me
He's gone.

Josephine Hodson (13)
Hornsey School For Girls

Critical Condition

I am in hospital, I feel like I'm dying
I must be dreaming, I feel like I'm flying
Everything around me is plain, white as snow
I'm remembering what happened, only a week ago

I'm hopeless, like a poor injured puppy
I'm lying here in pain, staring at the sky
I keep on wondering *will I die?*

My life is over, I can feel it
I'm looking back over my life, bit by bit
Could this be the end? Could this be it?

Sinead Ormonde (13)
Hornsey School For Girls

Who Am I?

There I was sitting on the cold, frosty pitch,
Waiting to be kicked,
I was in-between Giggs and Nistelrooy,
Waiting to be hammered back the other way,
Preeh, preeh,
The whistle blew
And then I flew,
I was being banged on the crossbar,
Smashed in the mud,
Kicked to the crowd
And dug with a stud.
Oh no, it started to rain,
I was already in enough pain,
I had been whacked into a net,
Feeling so very cold and wet.
People started cheering,
Whistle, the other team started staring.

Siama Ayiaz (13)
Hornsey School For Girls

My Favourite Book

I lay flat and still, lifeless on my hospital bed,
Remembering my mother and what she said.
I look at the spider in his web,
Small but quiet but his will so big.
The room is blue and calm,
I hear the nurses moving around outside.
Could it be my book is closing?
Is it true that I am dying?

Fatima Niazi (12)
Hornsey School For Girls

Remember Those Days

I stared at the gun in my hand
Pointed towards the strange face
I stopped and thought of good times
I shared with him
He was the light that shone in my life
I can remember when we were in the old house
And the accident that ruined his life

I could hear the doctor muttering
Like a comedian talking on and on
When I looked up in the clouds
I remembered when he and I used to watch the clouds
Till the sunlight

Then I saw the clouds moving
And heard him laugh as we shared jokes
I looked down at the dead body

Watching insects crawling on it
As the wind blew the leaves on the ground

Then I saw his little face smiling again
Like the bright sun.

Linda Mulungi (12)
Hornsey School For Girls

Secrets!

One day I saw my neighbour digging up her nose,
One day I saw my friend picking her toes.
One day I saw my grandpa licking his cereal bowl,
One day I saw my grandma picking her mole.
One day I saw my sister sleep-talking,
One day I saw my brother sleepwalking.
I have a secret which I cannot share!

Shazeda Uddin (12)
Hornsey School For Girls

Sunrise

The sun rising in the morning sky,
So amazing that all I can do is sigh,
Colours so light
Colours so bright

Yellow like honey,
Red like fire,
Brown like the coloured leaves in autumn,
Blue like the deep coloured ocean,
The clouds moving all in slow motion.

The sky is clear,
So much I can see and hear,
Children laughing in the meadows,
There should be no human lurking in the shadows.

For this is a beautiful day,
Look up at the bright sky,
That's what I say.

Aasiyah Oozeer (12)
Hornsey School For Girls

We Are Connected!

We are connected, no matter what colour we are,
If we are playing at home or rocking to music in the car.
We are connected, blue, white, black or pink,
We are connected in the way we think.
We are connected in many ways,
Our colour should not determine the way we get paid.
We are connected in the transport we take,
Whether we take a bus or take a boat through the lake.
We are connected!

Symone Prince (11)
Hornsey School For Girls

Colours

The bright bold colours of the sky,
From morn till nigh.
Shining colours from the sun,
Bright and gold, but what if there was none?

The purple, red and blue,
In the sky as if it was new.
The sun setting below the horizon,
A new day begins from morn.

Watching colours appear,
Then they soon will disappear,
There is only one chance,
To see the beautiful colours, then you soon will be in a trance.

Thinking about colours such as
Gold, orange, yellow, red, blue, purple,
In the sky and rainbow colours in the rain,
Watching the sunrise and the sunset down the lane.

The autumn leaves fall from trees,
They fall as if it was free.
Swaying from side to side,
Like it was dancing around.

Their colours fresh and bright,
Reflecting in the light.
Red, brown, yellow, pale green,
All the colours to be seen.

Trees are bare and leaves are everywhere,
Leaves are here and there.
Dropping from the sky as if it was snow,
The sun is low,
Making the Earth in a dimmed glow.

Siu-Mei Zhen (12)
Hornsey School For Girls

His Star

Lying there in his coffin,
Like a stone with no feeling, no emotion,
Unaware of the upset he has caused,
Like my world has come to an end.

Not that it is his fault,
He doesn't know our worries of him,
But now he has gone forever,
Like when you see somebody leave on the train.

I looked for his star,
A sign of him going to Heaven,
I saw it, the brightest one,
Like one of his eyes twinkling.

It has not sunk in yet,
I just don't want to think about it,
When I do, I just start to cry,
What's the use? It doesn't help.

At the funeral, I had to think,
About him, his life, his friends,
I didn't think it would be too bad,
But it was.

I have accepted it, although I don't want to,
At least he had a good life,
It is still so sad, it's miserable,
Although he doesn't want us to cry.

People do not understand,
They try to comfort me,
But I just want to be alone,
To think about him and his star.

Yasmin Wright (12)
Hornsey School For Girls

Untitled

As I stepped foot in the lot, I froze,
Bang! Bang! Bang!
I heard three bullets shoot out like fireworks on show,
I saw him grip gravel,
As if he was trying to hold on to his life.
But I knew he was going to let go,
Then his head hit the ground.
I wished he wouldn't die,
But then I remembered the sunsets
And realised his sun had set.
The blood,
The droning noise of the sirens,
I felt the air smacking my face,
Like when teachers clap their hands for quiet,
What a peaceful yet tense silence,
I feel emotions, anger, sadness . . . pain.
I'm like a confused turtle coming up to surface
And being blinded by lights.
His face as pale as snow and as cold as ice.
I smell the stale cigarettes on his shirt,
I'm desperate for water, my mouth dry as the Sahara.
I have a cramp in my throat,
Like a knot tied in a rope.
It's not his time,
Why did he have to go?

Simmone Robotham (12)
Hornsey School For Girls

Never Again

I looked at him
I looked straight into his eyes
I saw it, I saw the hurt and the pain in him
Like a stray, abandoned kitten
So cold and full of fear
I have never seen that in him
He's just so tough, he's just so tough
But now I know everyone has a soft side
Even a cold-blooded murderer has a soft side.

I saw him pull out the gun, why?
Why did he do it?
He knew they would shoot as soon as they saw it
But he did it
Bang! Bang! They shot him
I saw the bullets, the deadly bullets
Shooting as fast as sound towards him
He dropped to the ground
I saw the blood trickling down his neck
Like water vapour condensing on a cold window.

I can feel the wet, moist, hot sweat trickling down my face
Like a Caribbean storm
Then I saw him drop, drop for good
I'm never gonna see him again
I'm never gonna hear him swear again
I'm never gonna touch him again
I've lost him, I've lost him for good.

Bailsabe Mebrate (13)
Hornsey School For Girls

Tick-Tock

Beep, beep, beep
The heart monitor beeped as if it was counting the seconds
I had left to live.

Squeak, squeak, squeak
The nurses' rubber-soled shoes squeaked through the corridor
like little mice.

Mumble, mumble, mumble
The doctors mumbled to each other like bees at work,
Unsure of whether I could hear them or not.
Then all of a sudden,
The beeping got faster,
The squeaking got louder,
The mumbles turned to shouts,
What was happening?
Things whirled around me,
Lights got brighter.
Things blurred and things slowed down,
All the pain went away,
My body lifted from the bed
And I looked down on myself lying there,
'Time of death, 9.47.'

Aisling Davies (13)
Hornsey School For Girls

All About Me!

S is for Shaneka, yes that's me.
H is for happy and that's what I am.
A is for angel, that's what my mum calls me.
N is for naughty, I try not to be bad.
E is for eyes, so we can all see.
K is for kindness, I will always try to give.
A is for always, I will always try hard.

Shaneka Wellington (11)
Hornsey School For Girls

Johnny's Last Thoughts

Is this more painful than when my father beats me?
Is this better than being at home?
When my mother doesn't even know I exist
I feel so numb
Yet so delicate
I see red
I wonder
I wonder if this is the end
I feel so miserable
I don't want to die
Most things in my life haven't been joyful
There's lots of things I wanted to do
But now I won't get the chance
When people talk to me, it's like they are miming
Through the window I can see an ambulance
And some police cars parked outside
It seems like hundreds going past
I could just about see the sky
It looked as if it was going to come and swallow me up
I felt as if I were staring into nothingness
As the room goes an empty black.

Miriam Zaatri (13)
Hornsey School For Girls

She Drives Me Mad!

She drives me mad! She drives me nuts!
But she's the only one I have.
She can be sweet, she can be kind,
She messes my room most of the time.
She likes to borrow or so it's called,
I call it taking but that's not all,
She makes me laugh or sometimes sigh,
We always have our special times,
At the end of the day, she's a big part of my life,
Because she's my sister and that's no lie!

Claire Pavlouris (11)
Hornsey School For Girls

Dying

I felt the bullet travel inside me,
Then there was silence.
I could hear the trees rustling,
A newspaper scattering in the wind.
I heard the fuzz's sirens,
People screaming and wailing.
I heard people running towards me,
Like an elephant thudding on the jungle ground.

I heard my friend, Ponyboy shouting from a distance,
Like an echo drifting away.
I felt the wind blowing in all directions,
Like a tornado rushing away.

I opened my eyes,
I saw my friend's tears.
I felt his smooth, greasy hair,
I touched his chest,
I saw red trickling blood.

I sensed death coming to get me.

Fahmida Begum Hussain (13)
Hornsey School For Girls

Nectar

As I lay stiff in my bed watching a bee suck the nectar from
A lily outside my hospital window,
I heard the steps of people walking past my room,
The click clacking of the shoes on the marble floor,
Like the drip dripping of a tap,
The smell of the roses in my room,
I never realised how beautiful the smell of roses are
And how beautiful sunsets are, the pinks, the oranges spread
                                        like a rainbow,
The cool breeze outside softly moves the stained net curtain,
The rain hits the floor like a constant waterfall,
As the sun glows from behind the clouds like a golden coin.

Naomi Carty (12)
Hornsey School For Girls

Johnny Dying

Does this hurt me more than my father hits me?
I can't tell.
I can't feel half of me.
I hear the nurses talking,
Like a mouse squeaking in my head.

I keep focusing, my eyes on my still shadow,
That body can't have been mine,
Like a frozen statue.

I could see Ponyboy's face,
Wet with tears,
Like a wet dog that had just been outside in the rain.

I continued touching the bed I was lying in,
Which was smooth,
It was like a soft, silky dress.

Suddenly the empty room went pitch-black.

Nadia Malik (12)
Hornsey School For Girls

My Gang

Death is upon me, I cannot hide,
I don't want to go, I cannot tell a lie.
When it comes, all I want to do is run,
Run far away and jump into the sun.
Death is upon me, I cannot hide,
But since it's found me, I can no longer stay alive.

Bullets chase me and puncture my soul,
Fire burns me and for what? I don't know.
They don't come to me, they get to others,
But what they don't know is they're so close, they're brothers.
They both lie underground still as a wall,
As my heart slowly falls.

Bianca Julien (12)
Hornsey School For Girls

Being In A Gang

Tears drip, drip out of my eye
Like rain from the sky

Still my heart aches like fire
Burning my skin
Anger still rages inside me
Like a volcano about to explode

As soon as I touched the ground
My body felt numb

My gun felt cold and hard
Like a heavy rock

I can smell the cold-hearted flowers
Sway in the air

They always said a kid like me
Was truly rare.

Shadayna Jauffur (12)
Hornsey School For Girls

Worth It

These hours are countless,
So I won't try.

These days are endless,
So I won't begin.

If I stop breathing,
If you stop breathing,
If we all stop breathing.

We could put life out of business
And get death a pay rise.

Lauren Pratt (13)
Hornsey School For Girls

Never

Blood seeps across the dirty, grey snow
Still warm from the breast of a bird
Shot dead
Alone
The cold winter air feels somehow clean
Footsteps of the hunter's boots
Still new in the snow
His excuses
Formed in his head
From the secret guilt
Of taking innocent lives
Won't bring the bird back
Won't feed her children
Cold in the nest
An icy wind blows
Ruffling her feathers
As the pool of blood spreads
Ebony trees
Black and bare
Against the sky
Put in mind
The summer's gone
With the bird in the trees
Never again
Never to feel the rush of the wind
Never to touch the deep open sky
Silent heart
Never to beat again
Never.

Raina vonAhn (12)
Hornsey School For Girls

My Number 1!

His skin . . .
His golden-brown skin
That soft touch
That smell of cocoa butter.

His hair . . .
His newly greased and cornrowed hair
The beads at the end of his braids
That parting, oh how straight it is!

His eyes . . .
Oh how the sun shines through them
How the sun sets in them
The look of green that shines in your eyes
When his eyes set on yours.

And that voice . . .
How it sounded when it was breaking
How it sounds now it's broken
And the way it tickles your ears when you hear it.

. . . He's my number 1!

Danyelle Myall-Kirton (13)
Hornsey School For Girls

Respect

R espect people in every way.
E thnic backgrounds or wherever they're from.
S ensible, not shy, kind.
P lay with others nicely.
E xpect respect, if you give respect.
C are for others, don't judge them.
T alk to people in a nice way
    and remember . . .
    Respect!

Kelle Salle (13)
Hornsey School For Girls

Seasons

W inter, winter, the coldest time of year
I ce and snow is always there.
N ever hot and never sunny.
T rees are bare and always skinny.
E very day the same old story.
R eally, really a cold, cold story.

S pring, spring comes once a year.
P lants and flowers start to grow.
R ain begins to disappear.
I ce and snow never appear.
N ew beginnings and a fresh start.
G etting ready for a hot, hot summer.

S unny and hot every day.
U nbearably hot.
M ore flowers start to grow.
M ore vegetables grow.
E very day the same hot story.
R eally a hot, hot story.

A utumn's here and the trees go bare.
U nbearably windy.
T ruly cold and windy.
U nbelievably cold.
M uch too cold to go outside.
N ever seems to get warmer, and nearly time for winter.

Rehmat Madari (13)
Hornsey School For Girls

Like A Flower

Like a flower we are
We come so far
From the ground
And so we grow
And we fade but we
Come back again
And so we have one
Part of our life
That is fun
But for a flower
It gets watered
And is just growing
So it is just laying there
So if you see a flower
Remember how it first became.

Shermin Hassan (12)
Hornsey School For Girls

Love Is . . .

Love is . . .
Love is you
Love is me
Love is life
Love is true
Love is blind
Love is trust
Love is bright
Love is everything surrounding you,
A glance of you puts a smile on my face
And a shine in my eyes,
A day without seeing you feels like I'm in Hell.

Fatima Ullan (13)
Hornsey School For Girls

What Can I Do?

What can I do?
I'm sitting in the middle of the room
No one's home except me and darkness
Everywhere is dark, I can't see anything
Only the moon which shines the room
My parents gone to a party
Why couldn't I go?
I'm waiting for them for hours
When are they going to come?
1, 2, 3, 4, 5, they're not here yet
Don't they ever care about me?
I feel lonely and scared
I love my parents but they hate me
I feel cold and worried
It is 10.30pm, when are they returning home?
Ding dong.

Meral Ozdil (13)
Hornsey School For Girls

Fruit And Vegetables Poem

Cauliflowers fluffy and
Cabbages green
Strawberries sweeter
Than any I've seen
Beetroot purple and onions white
All grow steadily day and night!

The apples are ripe
The plums are red
Broad beans are sleeping
In a blankety bed!

Balkis El-Khalaf (12)
Hornsey School For Girls

Don't Hate, Appreciate

I don't like being deceived or lied to
I don't like it when people use me and take me for a fool
I don't like having false assumptions made about me
Do any of the above and I'm going to set my wicked side free

When people tell me they love me and it's not true
It just makes me want to go all blue
If you don't like me, then just tell me so
Don't bottle it up and think I don't have a clue

I don't like bad-minded people
Who just look at you and all they can do is screw
When someone says they care
And when you look at them it's as if they were talking to the air

I don't understand why people have to lie
It's as if they think you're gonna cry
If I don't like someone, I'll tell them bye
I don't just hate and then they wonder why

So don't lie to me or take me for a fool
'Cause at the end of the day, it don't hurt me, it's all cool.

Don't hate, appreciate.

Danielle Allen (13)
Hornsey School For Girls

Love Is Like An Onion . . .

Once it's there and the next it's gone
Chopped up for life

It makes your eyes fill up with tears
And all you can see is a blurry view with unseen objects
Only a blur of them until you blink
Then it comes flying down like a waterfall
Just like someone you love

It's got a crispy outside
But on the inside, it's a stinger

It sticks to you even if you don't want it to
You can smell it like you have been munching it
Just like a lover, a lover doesn't have to be a boyfriend
Cousin, aunty, mum or dad
It can be anyone you want it to be

When it's gone, it's gone
Just like that onion when it's chopped up
It's chopped up, gone
But with time it doesn't stop sticking
It doesn't stop smelling
And you certainly don't stop loving.

Jolene Osborne (13)
Hornsey School For Girls

What Do I Want For Christmas?

What do I want for Christmas?
What would most 7-year-old girls want?
A pony,
Mum would say it's too expensive.
A video,
There is no point as I cannot see.
How about a climbing frame?
Too dangerous in my condition.
You see I'm a very special girl.

I lost my eyesight a year ago,
I lost my hair two months ago.
It's now just 2 weeks till Christmas.
What do I want for Christmas?
To be alive.

Jo Pidsley (13)
Hornsey School For Girls

Friendship Is A Jewel

Our friendship is like a star,
Which will never lose its sparkle and forever stay.
Our friendship is like an iron chain,
Which will stay linked together through ups and down.
Your company is richer than any king's robe,
Your happiness is more meaningful than any crystal.
Roses will wither away
And money may lose its value.
But our friendship was created to keep,
Because your friendship to me is like a precious jewel,
That I'll treasure forever.

Pooja Raval (13)
Hornsey School For Girls

Memories

What is a memory?
Why do we have them?
It's like a never-ending flame that sparks up deepening the wound.
What's the point?
It must happen for a reason,
Everything happens for a reason.
It brings the past in line with the present
Or does it take the present back into the past?
Who knows.
Do memories help us heal wounds?
Knowing that something spiritual exists around you
Is better than it not existing at all.
Right?
Writing this poem brings back memories,
But that's a good thing.
Right?
What is a memory?
Why do we have them?
No one can answer that question
And yet we experience them every day.
I can answer it.
A memory is a push from the past into the future,
That's what a memory is.

Reema Jethwa (13)
Hornsey School For Girls

The Jungle

I am looking in the jungle,
What do I see?
A monkey, a snake and a spider looking at me,
It looked very scary so I decided to run,
But then I realised they just wanted to have fun,
We played hide-and-seek, so I hid in the leaves,
Where I met a flying bird and a talking tree.
The tree said hello and the bird said goodbye,
She pecked me on my ear, so I started to cry.
Her squawk was scary so I started to run,
I jumped in the air and fell on my bum,
But then I was thinking,
Oh gosh, am I sinking?
She sounded like a marching band,
Saying, 'Ha, ha, ha, you're in quicksand.'

Sophie Francis (13)
Hornsey School For Girls

Goodbye . . .

Goodbye is the word that
You never want to hear
And when it hits
You have no choice but to fear
The love, the pain
You might never see them again
The bond that was so tight
And now you're on that next flight
It's always that someone that you love the most
And the only thing you might have left is their ghost
Wishing and wondering why they have gone
Is goodbye just a word? No, it's a feeling . . .
A sad love song . . .

Shakirah Hunte (13)
Hornsey School For Girls

My Grandad

I miss you even though I hardly knew you
The fact that you're gone, I can't accept it's true
I believe that there's a reason you're gone
In our hearts we are as one
I just wanna feel your tender touch
You've given me so little and it feels like so much
No matter how much I try, I can't let go
But your memories are really good to know

Staring at the sky
Makes me wanna cry
It's so hard to say goodbye
There's no need to wonder why
Whenever I feel bad
I think of my grandad

I miss sitting with you in your chair
I miss the soft touch of your curly hair
I miss you in each and every way
Thinking of you every step I take, every single day
I miss going to see my grandad
And most of all I miss the bond we had.

Shaneka D'aguilar Rock (13)
Hornsey School For Girls

Sadieann

S is for special, that's me.
A is for ambitious, that's what I want to be.
D is for determined never to give up.
I is for important to always do my best.
E is for education, that's why I go to school.
A is for ability, always work hard.
N is for natural, always be myself.
N is for nice, that's what I am to everyone.

Sadieann Bassaragh (12)
Hornsey School For Girls

Failure Is Not An Option!

Failure is not an option
I will not fear, falter
I shall succeed
My perception is altered
I do believe
Faith is strong
Nothing shall bar my way!
From this conviction no friction
This is my day
I walk so tall, ascending
I stand so high
Earth below me, revolving
Above the sky
I feel no fear to be here
Is O' so fine
Shining brightly like sunlight
Inside my mind.

Chandni Lashamee Buljhoo (12)
Hornsey School For Girls

The Unhappy Girl

A long time ago in a far-off town
There was a girl who always frowned
The people always told her to cheer up
She just told them to shut up
Her parents were always miserable
They wanted a new child
The foster people told them they were wild
You can't just abandon your child
They were all surprised
When the circus came to town
Because they turned her frown upside down.

Naomi Simmons (11)
Hornsey School For Girls

Cold

This is the winter
Everybody's bitter
Sun never coming out, never better
Cold, cold

It's hailstones, raining
Groaning and pouring
Sun has gone, no more fun, it's changing
Cold, cold

Gees, I'm freezing
Weather is not pleasing
Time to get a tissue, I'm sneezing
Cold, cold

This is the winter
Everybody's bitter
Sun never coming out, never better
Cold, cold, cold!

Cheneiss Bonitto (12)
Hornsey School For Girls

Midnight

I have a cat,
His name is Midnight,
He sleeps from day till dusk,
Only then does he come out,
To slip beneath the trees,
He waits,
Praying for a mouse,
A dog's bark fills the air,
He stops and waits,
Then thinks himself away.

Emma Larkin-Tannett (11)
Hornsey School For Girls

War

War is the sound of fathers dying,
Mothers screaming
And children crying,
War.

War is a howling underworld,
Where the smell of death suffocates you
And where demons steal your soul,
War.

War is a black sea,
Where the tears of God bottle you up
And your blood begins to boil,
War.

War is a dangerous forest,
Where a sinister laugh tears heart
And eyes shriek with death,
War.

There is no more war,
There is just silence
And destruction lay still,
When will we stop this war?

Temisanren Akitikori (11)
Hornsey School For Girls

Can't Switch Off

I cuddle up, I wrap up warm
I'm ready to go to bed
I lie and look into wilderness
Thoughts jump into my head

I sleep among the bed of stars
I watch the night go by
I turn my cushion right around
I let out a tired sigh

I close my eyes
I think of things
I turn my bedside light off
Who knows what the night-time brings

I look out of my window
I see the trees rustle by
It looks so cold outside
And there . . . there I lie

Can't switch off
It's almost 12 o'clock
And then all I hear is my clock
Tick-tock, tick-tock, tick-tock . . .

Tuesday Critchfield (12)
Hornsey School For Girls

The Last Words!

Beware! Beware!
Because I am here, I am here.

I can swift through your body,
I can scare you out of your skin,
I can go through your mind,
Because all I am is thin air.

You cannot see me,
Because I am not there,
You might have guessed,
That I am a ghost in despair.

The last words I must say,
Before I leave,
Are the same words I said
Before my death:
'Please send flowers to my grave.'

Thaminah Ali (12)
Hornsey School For Girls

War And Peace

Two things that can change your life forever!
Well, there's . . .

W ar is a living nightmare, 24 hours a day
A ggravation, hurt and pain
R etreating, you wish, they'll never go away

Whereas . . .

P eace is lovingness, happiness and freedom
E asy, after all it's not hard to be nice
A ggravation free
C harity is important although money is not
E ver wondered what the world would be like with peace
   roaming the streets?

Medina Choudhry (12)
Hornsey School For Girls

The Life Dance

The life dance,
You see it in the trees
And the life song,
You hear it in the wind.

Life is playing its tune everywhere,
It is dancing to the beat of the world.
Through fields of tulips and barley,
If we listen and watch we will realise . . .

That the life dance,
Is among our very trees
And the life song,
Is heard among the wind.

Life is singing and dancing,
Wherever you go,
Belting out its song around the world,
Dancing passionately with the moon and the sun,
Life is with us, around us,
Singing beside us,
Dancing above us,
Living with us.

We sense it in the sun, we breathe in the grass and we know . . .

That the life dance,
Is among our very trees
And the life song,
Is heard among the wind
And we know that life is with us.
Cherish it.

Leah Callender-Crowe (12)
Hornsey School For Girls

Peace

There's never *peace* in our house
It's the noisiest house on the block
From morning until night-time
We shout, we scream and we fuss
We blast out music with volume
The TV tries to compete
And in the middle of all the noise
You might hear my mother screech

'I need 5 minutes peace
I need time to be alone
I wish you kids would go to bed
And leave me on my own'

The trouble is we've heard it
A million times before
So no one takes any notice
And we usually scream some more

The worst time is at dinner
When we fight over plates of food
We fight to get the best seat
And the best view of the TV on the wall
We fight over who will do the dishes
Who will put them away
And in the midst of all the disturbance
You can just hear my mother say

'I need 5 minutes peace
I need time to be alone
I wish you kids would go to bed
And leave me on my own'

We fight to use the bathroom
We battle to brush our teeth
We clash to use the mirror
We compete to wash our feet

And then at five to ten the house just settles down
My mother turns the TV off
The CD volume down
Out comes the magazine, she brought on her last trip to town
She makes herself a cocoa and then she settles down

She'll often fall asleep there
And you might hear her mutter in her sleep

'I finally got 5 minutes peace
I've finally been left alone
My kids have now all gone to bed
And left me on my own.'

Phillippa Tappin (12)
Hornsey School For Girls

Arguing With My Sister

Have you got a sister?
I do,
It's such a pain,
Her name is Romily,
I'll try to explain.

She borrows my stuff
And wears my tops,
She uses her fists,
Not to mention her feet,
There's more to add to the list.

When I do bad stuff,
She tells my mum,
She sticks up for my little sis,
When I know she's in the wrong.

Do you have a sister?
I do,
It's such a pain,
Her name is Romily,
I'll try to explain.

Kessia Hammett (12)
Hornsey School For Girls

Reality

Women,
Often a minority,
Often misjudged,
Often misunderstood,
Sometimes loved,
Women,
Treated unfairly in the human race,
Come on women,
We can do it,
If we B&Q it,
This poem's no joke,
This is reality.

Men,
Often a majority,
Often they misjudge,
Often misunderstanding,
Sometimes loving,
Men,
Think they're the best in the human race,
Come on men,
Sort it out,
Equality's what this world's about,
This poem's no joke,
This is reality.

Oonagh O'Connor (13)
Hornsey School For Girls

One For The Baby

This is for the baby,
Precious is his name,
This is for the baby,
Who fought for life in vain.

This is for the baby,
Who made his cousin proud,
This is for the baby,
Now sleeping on his cloud.

This is for the baby,
Strong and O so true,
This is for the baby,
Because I'm still missing you . . .

This is for the baby,
In Heaven and above,
This is for the baby,
Who filled the world with love.

But if this happy, loving child
Had fought another day,
Who knows what would have happened,
Only he could say.

So tell me please,
Why on earth
Is he not here still?
And why is there an empty space
That only he can fill?

Ciara McGlacken (12)
Hornsey School For Girls

Gone

She's gone, she's gone, she's left, she's gone
They picked her up like a puppet on strings
And away she was flung.

We always thought she was OK, she was the happy one,
But one day she just snapped and disappeared
And away she was gone.

The rain and the storm just washed her away,
She never told, she couldn't stay,
The icy cold must have frozen her to death,
She'd had enough and so she just left.

She's gone, she's gone, she's left, she's gone,
We always thought she was so strong,
Oh, I didn't know we could be so wrong
And now away she's gone.

Sinead Khan (12)
Hornsey School For Girls

The Midnight Silence

I was in the deep, dark forest,
I heard no sound,
Loudly, my heart started to pound,
Dead silence made me want to be found,
There was no human habitations around,
It was December, the darkest evening of the year,
I was alone, lost and my mind covered with fear,
A silver, salt droplet ran down my cheek, it was a tear,
This nightmare was endless but I hoped it ended now and here,
Then a shadow lurked,
I heard four paws crawling softly as it was put to work,
I heard a growl and a howl,
I cried, I wanted to hide,
But then my heart stopped as I saw two emerald eyes
Stare in the dark shadows,
A figure appeared, it was a . . .

Marian Ali (14)
Hornsey School For Girls

The Power Of A Lighted Candle

A lighted candle is a long white stick,
A silent fire,
The heart of a volcano,
A bundle of snow,
Like a miracle about to happen,
The key to happiness,
The door to conquer darkness,
The way to enlightenment,
The warmth of the sun,
It lights the way to Heaven,
Our friend in solitude,
It sustains us in misery,
Our companion when friendless,
It's our ornament amongst friends,
And an armour against enemies,
But most of all it's the thick, white warmth of a loving home.

Ayan Jimale (13)
Hornsey School For Girls

The Slogan Song

All these slogans singing to me . . .
Is it because I'm worth it?
I can taste the rainbow, bazooka, get the urge
Maybe it's because I'm born with it.

It's like I'm full of volcanicity -
Hey, slogans give me wings!
I'm thinking Oxy but I'm getting 'Give me juice'
It's not Terry going mad - it's me!
Once I pop with these slogans I just can't stop -
Those who can, teach.

I'm reading through this poem now, it's good for life,
It's quoting me happy and life tastes good,
There's just one more thing - oh yeah,
I'm lovin' it!

Louisa Casson (12)
Hornsey School For Girls

Realised

All the hurt,
All the pain,
It was time to move on
And see what I had to gain.

From this incident,
From this time,
I now know,
What was not to be mine.

The troubles left me,
Filling me with bliss,
As I let it all go,
Pain, I will not miss.

As you walked away,
From my life,
I knew that you
Where only being nice.

I thought I felt something,
But it wasn't real,
It was really a good thing,
This relationship is sealed.

I felt nothing as you stepped out my life,
From then I knew,
For then I realised,
I did not love you.

Husna Khatri (11)
Hornsey School For Girls

Hand In Hand

Together we stand,
Hand in hand,
We are but one . . .

But wait,
I don't understand?
Our world is not all love,
There is hate,
There is war,
There is crime.

But *why*?
Why can't we stand
Hand in hand?
Why not?
Why instead do we kill and hate?
We need some help!
Help from above,
God please help us,
Help us to love.

Why is there starvation?
Can't we all just share?
Don't just stand there!
Help us please!
All we can do is stare.

So why can't we stand,
Hand in hand,
Together,
Forever.

Forever?

Helena Marrion-Cole (12)
Hornsey School For Girls

My Sister Is An Angel

My sister is an angel
She's always really good
But I'm not like that at all
I never do what I should

I once had a dream about her
She floated over my head
Then she flew around my room
And then onto my bed

She gave me a cheeky grin
Her pearly teeth glinting bright
Then she took me by my hands
And we flew into the night

We flew into the forest
Getting branches in our hair
Then into a dark, dark cave
Where we saw a bear!

That was enough adventure
So she said she'd take me home
Then she took me to my bed
Where I lay there all alone.

Charlotte Barnes-Thomas (12)
Hornsey School For Girls

My Strudel

Where's the strudel?
Add the poodle
Puppy-dog's legs
And 12 outside pegs
Around, around
The school bells go
Tiptoe, tiptoe
Join in the Chinese rice
Add lots of spice
Cat's tail under a stone
And don't forget the mobile phone
Around, around
The school bells go
Tiptoe, tiptoe
Join in with the flow
Two milk teeth
And roast beef
Lots of honey
Then add the squashed bunny
Around, around
The school bells go
Tiptoe, tiptoe
Join in with the flow.

Natalie Harriott (11)
Hornsey School For Girls

The Dreamer Of Peace

The sky was towering overhead and the marshmallow
                    clouds moved swiftly in harmony.
She sat, gazed and listened, rhythms inside her body disturbed.
The sky, a blue, a colour so intense that she couldn't describe.
She lay down, her slender fingers running to and fro,
Between the delicately, smoothly sculptured sand.
The golden surfaced horizon, spread out as if parallel with
                    the ocean for eternity.
She was part of the velvetness of the sky,
A tiny part in the glittering stars guiding her through the breeze
                    of the soft air.
She had been deeply immersed in the rhythms of the Earth,
As if the elements were one with her,
To feel the pulse of life in the planet, in herself, strong,
                    deep and vibrant.
She was gifted, blessed with a part of hope and love.
To experience the impossibilities of all and the awakening
                    shiver of dawn.
To be in touch with elements, having them under her command.
Is as though the essence of life, blown individually onto
                    each and every form.
And like blazing fire, the desire, begins to pace . . .

Zam Zam Ali (12)
Hornsey School For Girls

Will Our Wishes Turn Out Positive?

We wished for happiness and became unhappy
We wished for joy and became miserable
We wished to be outgoing and became self-centred
We wished for friendship and became enemies

We wished for relaxation and got the shakes
We wished for confidence and became uncertain
We wished for bravery and became afraid
We wished for certainty and became unsure

We wished for strength and felt weak
We wished to make conversation easier and made it harder
We wished for warmth and lost our cool
We wished for coolness and lost our warmth

We wished to feel heavenly and knew Hell
We wished to forget and were reminded
We wished for freedom and became slaves
We wished for power and were powerless

We wished to erase problems and saw them multiply
We wished to forgive and became unforgiving
We wished for love and became hateful
We wished that our wishes would one day turn out *positive*.

Jihan Shatiry (13)
Hornsey School For Girls

Unique Recipe

Ingredients

1 cup full of kindness
500g of laughter and happiness
2 buckets of air to breathe
40g of quietness to sleep
1 dollop of joy and jokes
14 teaspoons of practise of singing and dancing
1 bucket of fun and play
5 cups of smartness
2 cups of sadness
3 spoons of healthy bones
6 buckets of food to cool the mood
1 chopped banana
2 drops each of England and Ghana

Method

Mix the happiness and the laughter with the kindness
And the smartness, add the sadness
Stir in the air then go to the funfair
Pour in the singing and dancing
Add some fun games but don't take the blame
Then put in the drops of England and Ghana
Add the pieces of chopped banana
Next put in 3 spoons of healthy bones
We can never miss the joy and jokes
After that add together the quietness to sleep and dream
Make sure you see the steam
Pop it in the oven for 10 to 20 minutes
And out comes a unique cake
You did not make a mistake!

Abigail Ayensu (11)
Hornsey School For Girls

The Girl

She arrives at 8.15 every morning,
Her homework done, her work so neat.
She waits for five minutes then she goes in.
She sits in her isolated seat.

She looks around, it's the same every day,
The room is so clean and tidy.
She tells herself, 'I want it this way.'
But deep down she's dying in anguish.

Again her classmates are fashionably late,
She lets them know what she thinks of them,
They just reply, 'Don't hate, appreciate!'
But this only makes things worse.

Day after day the pain and anger wells up,
She doesn't know it's coming yet.
It's getting bigger and soon going to erupt,
It's not her fault she constantly thinks.

Her anticipated day came with a bang,
People still try to forget it,
She wasn't normal, never in a gang,
Yet in the news people gave it that theme.

It's only now that people see how important it is,
Everybody must have at least one friend.
If you don't, you'll sadly end up,
As that poor and helpless girl did.

Symone La Touche (13)
Hornsey School For Girls

Wonders Of The World

Shades upon shades of aquamarines and sapphires,
I look upon the golden seabed,
While the warm summer sun spreads its golden rays upon me,
Laps upon laps of gentle water,
I gently touched the soft wet skin,
As I swam with beautiful dolphins.

Shades upon shades of ambers and golds,
I look upon the golden sunset,
While pearl-white swans sing heartbreaking love songs,
I gaze upon the magnificent horizon,
Oh how I long to swim to my furthest dream,
But now wanting to disturb the beautiful animals,
I never moved from my sandy dream.

Shades upon shades of diamonds and opals,
I look upon the crystal chasms,
As polar bears walk gracefully like kings,
While the penguins through the snow,
I slip and slide,
As I journey to the South Pole.

Shades upon shades of the colours of the rainbow,
I gallop gracefully on my Romany-coloured brown hew horse,
While all the flowers look like dots of colour,
As the gentle breezing of the wind caresses on my face,
Flowers and sunshine equals this wonder,
These are the wonders of the world.

Yusra Murshid (11)
Hornsey School For Girls

Imagine

Imagine a world that's never been seen
Been touched by a human soul within
Close your eyes then open them again . . .
 Imagine

What beautiful place I can see
It's just it and me
You can't shrug and moan
Because it's my very own . . .
 Imagine

You can have yours too
Do anything you want to do
Just do one thing for me . . .

Imagine a world that's never been seen
Been touched by a human soul within
Close your eyes then open them again . . .
 Imagine.

Awawu Olaitan-Salami (12)
Hornsey School For Girls

Helpless, Confused

Helpless, confused,
Didn't know what to do, panic, panic!
Going round and round the world in circles,
Dark, lonely woodland forest,
Scared, trembling with fear,
Quivering, shaking, help . . . argh!
Surface muddy, sinking through,
Sheltering below tall trees,
Danger, risk, jungle, moving!
Loud noises, dogs barking,
Parents shouting, children screaming,
Neighbourhood coming, all looking,
Safe at last!

Zahrah Khan (11)
Islamia Girls' School

A Deadly Trap

Thirsty, hungry, dizzy, stinging, help;
Rushing, thoughts, help, home, water, anyone, help,
I'm helpless, I'm falling, I'm dizzy, I'm shouting, no movement, help;
Feeling lost, I look again, but no one, no life, will I get home? Help;
Panic, I'm dying, it's hurting, so quiet, just me screaming help.
It's quiet, no one, no life, no breeze, no movement, just me, help.
Fallen trees surrounding me, tripping me, *help!*
Hot sun, need water, need shade, I'm sizzling, I'm furious,
                                        where's help?
No life, no insects, no plants, no animals, no people, no help.
Hungry, need food, please listen, my tummy, so much pain,
                                        oh God help;
No signals, I scream, no reply, still screaming, still no help,
I need water, I search high, low, still not found, I won't bother,
                                        there's no help,
My burning throat, my aching tummy, my stinging leg, my poor body,
My mobile's ringing, just before I'm out of hope, I pick up,
                                        'Please help, help.'

Bushra Al-Akra (11)
Islamia Girls' School

Terrible Terror . . .

Sandy: hot sand, yellow, dusty, tiny,
Hot: sweat, boiling inside me, 'Miya nahana hai,' water.
Big trees: green, big shadows, huge, nice fresh air.
Fire: red-hot, can kill, dangerous.
Blood-red: everywhere, disgusting and watery.
Eyes blurry: dizzy, half-blind, can't see properly, 'Ow!'
Feeling dizzy: can't move, eyes blurry, sleepy.
'Oliti.'
No help: scared, 'Narazz,' shouting, crying.
Dying: having pain, praying for help, sad to leave the Earth.
All alone: scared, frightened, useless for anything.
Hunger: tummy hurting, food, dizzy.
'Oliti.'

Noor Shibu (11)
Islamia Girls' School

I've Been Bitten!

Brain rattling, sweating, thinking fast
Pain, hurting, bleeding, pain getting worse
Dripping, boiling hot, sweating more
Red, going everywhere, isn't stopping
Lots of trees, small, big, medium
Cool breeze, little chill, cools me down
Birds whistling, owls tooting, birds all around
Green leaves surrounding me, dead leaves
Shouting help from anyone, hoping someone will come
Silence, not a sound, completely quiet
A person comes to my rescue, saves me from death
Picks me up from the ground, home at last
Home at last, still feel pain, doctor comes
Doctor helps the sting, the pains went away
I smile, I sing, I am happy, happy, happy
Relieved, I'm alive, with more life, more joy.

Armara Rowlands (11)
Islamia Girls' School

Hot And Dizzy

Drained, weak and no energy
My head unbalanced, hot like dipped in hot water
Blood dripping, making a puddle
Knees wobbling, about to faint
Screaming loudly so someone can hear
Sweaty face, knees swelling
Purple and blue
Pins and needles all over me
Sheltering above, tall trees with a hot breeze around me
Sinking down in a muddy surface
With vultures screaming above
Dogs barking, people running to help
People pushing buttons, texting
People phoning, bells ringing
Saved at last!

Anisa Khan (11)
Islamia Girls' School

Horror And Revulsion

As sharp as needles, the pain was unbearable.
Long scary branches towering over me.
Trees dancing around me
Floating like a leaf.
My mouth was as dry as the surface of a desert.
Light streaming through the trees.
I was alone like a pebble in a river.
Blue sky shining hope.
Convulsions flow through my body.
Fear creeping into my heart like a shadow.
Voices calling my name.
Gentle caress sweeps my face.

Aminah Akhtar (11)
Islamia Girls' School

Danger Of A Snake!

Beach with cold water, salty to taste,
Breezy, windy, with splashes of rain,
Hearing the hissing sound, legs and hands shivering with fright,
Deep, long, cloudy sky like an ocean floating by,
Pain, blood covered with red, dripping danger around.
Worried, home, needing to have dreamed,
Danger around,
Help,
Horrified, sweating because of fright, heart pounding,
Silent, peaceful, quiet, not a sound,
Faint, water, poisoned by a snake,
Run, run for life, snakes,
Safety, home, family and friends, Mum!

Alat Leelo (11)
Islamia Girls' School

Bitten By . . .

Surprised, terrified, full of horror
Heart pounding and beating quickly
Shivering, tense, my body vibrating
Panicked, worried and concerned
Dizzy, fainting, light-headed
Abandoned, deserted, afraid and unsafe
Despair, hopelessness and anxiety
Fearful, apprehensive and nervous
A dark, frightening, haunted forest
Strange, ghostly and full of terror
Tall, dark trees everywhere
Petrifying, lonely, creepy and dark
Tears of happiness, howling dogs
Relieved, calm, glad and relaxed
Dog disappears, cries of help, dog vanishes
Hope fades away and loneliness returns.

Shafaq Adnan (11)
Islamia Girls' School

A Dead End

Knife digging into me,
Pain surging through my leg.
Panic, going round in circles.
Blood leaking down warmly.
Blistering sun burning down,
Yellow continuous sand.
Humid smell stinging my nostrils.
Trees waving their branches in the breeze.
Silence drowning my ears.
Need help, panicking, don't know what to do,
Exhausted, dehydrated, headache.
Dying, heart throbbing, poison spreading . . .

Sarah Rhalem (11)
Islamia Girls' School

Frustrated, Help Needed!

Agonising pain,
I couldn't stand it!
Panic was taking over me!
My heart was pounding,
I didn't understand why it was meant to be,
Beautiful waterfalls lapped before me.
Large, tall trees all around me.
Suddenly
My sight went blind,
I felt something on my leg,
Oh it ached!
My head was spinning and whizzing,
Hope for existing was whittling,
The sound of the squirrel chittering,
The sound of the bird, singing,
All those sounds seemed far away,
I felt a lick on my cheek, my horse!
He made me climb on him and galloped away,
All of a sudden,
We saw a man in the distance,
He called the ambulance,
A few minutes later, an ambulance came rushing by,
My mum visited and said, 'If I could go back in time
I would have chosen to go with you.'

Muna Salah (11)
Islamia Girls' School

Pain And Panic

I remember being bitten by a cobra,
It was very distressing.
I was in a scorching desert,
Admiring the charming palm trees
And I didn't see the cobra,
Slithering towards me.
Its fangs sticking out of its mouth
And without me knowing it,
The cobra bit me.
I screamed,
But that was not a scream,
It was only a little squeal,
Pain was stirring through my body,
My legs felt weak
And every time I looked down,
I could see the floor getting closer and closer
And then I fainted.
When I woke up,
I found myself lying in bed,
In a gratified hospital,
With my leg bandaged
And my parents around me.
'Thank goodness it happened to me
Not to my parents,' I said.

Tasnim Limam (11)
Islamia Girls' School

Gripping Fear!

A pierce in my skin,
Heart beating with fear.
Red blood oozing with force,
Jumping up and down with panic.
Knees wobbly and energy drained,
Stomach squirming, vomit!
A cool, slight gust of wind,
Crumbly, rocky, mountain with
Sharp, stinging, fanged snakes.
A large crowd of lush green trees,
Energy drained, limping along.
Collapsing with tiredness, head whizzing,
Black-haired animal,
Exhausted, crows cawing.
Cries of help heard in the distance.
Yes! . . .
Help at last . . . Thank goodness!

Tahiya Afzel (11)
Islamia Girls' School

Agony

Panic, pounding in my ears,
'Mum,' I screamed, 'where are you?'
Icy blood gushing into my socks,
Staining them with red,
Agonising pain in my ankle.
The trees coming closer,
The sky pressing down,
Everything a blinding whirl of colour.
Ghostly footsteps,
Were they real or were they merely echoes of my life,
Telling me that my time had come?
The footsteps got louder and a shadow fell over me,
I looked up, the scene swimming in my eyes,
Help had come.

Safiya Sheikh (11)
Islamia Girls' School

Horrible Snake Bite!

That day strolling in the park,
What a sunny day I could say it was,
Hearing the sweet sound of birds chirping,
Bite! I screamed, I just could not get up,
I was sweating all over, feverish-like,
Everyone was huddling up to me,
Phones were on and texting, I knew I might die,
I felt like I had been stabbed with a knife,
Crowds and crowds of people all over was all I could see,
Blood, pain everywhere, I just could not stop screaming,
My heart pounding like mad, jumping and thumping,
Dizzy, my head was whizzing, I felt like I was blind,
Then I heard the sirens of an ambulance,
At last I'm safe!

Faiza Hussain (11)
Islamia Girls' School

Enemies Bite

Tried to stand, stumbling
Leg sore, red
Don't know what to do
Panicked
Hot all round my body
Speechless - huge, monstrous trees
Crunching leaves orange, yellow, red
Surrounding more enemies, more snakes
Jolt at crisp sounds around me
Before me, starting my way home
Feeling of relief
Safety coming
Someone appears to help me stay alive
Find trust amongst the jungle
My hero here at last.

Hanan Abdel-Khalek (11)
Islamia Girls' School

An Agonising Wait . . .

Pain, aching
Like a dagger plunged in arm -
See blood - bright red
Panic, feel alarmed
Feeling faint, head whizzing
Humid air
Birds cawing loudly
Too quiet for words
Exhausted - tired
Hear river rushing downfall
Crunching of leaves -
Footsteps in the distance
A surge of hope
Help arrived at last
Really tired now -
Finally in good hands
Alive and thankful.

Maymuna Osman (11)
Islamia Girls' School

Terrified And Alarmed!

Tall trees swaying side to side,
Warm breeze, blowing in my face,
Children crying, shouting and playing,
Blue skies, clouds and sun.
Pins and needle prickly and spiky,
Blood-red, slimy and sticky,
Headache, pains, stabbing knives, aching.
Dizzy, faint and lots of circles,
Cold, shivers and shaking,
Fear, scared and very frightened,
Nothing, silence, no one,
Man, tall, dark, helpful,
Grateful, thankful and alive.

Sarah Leslie (11)
Islamia Girls' School

Cats

Cats are furry to me
They sleep oh so silently
They sometimes have cat fights
But not in daylight
They like to play
They do it every day
I love cats
Much more adorable than rats
Cats chase mice
But the mice are as quick as ice
Cats nap at night
In their baskets nice and tight
Cats are clever at being bait
But the dogs get there too late
Cats are clever
That's why they never, ever, ever get caught!

Raquel Silva De Freitas (11)
La Sainte Union School

In The Park Alone

In the park alone,
Thunder and rain,
Freezing me to the bone.
Swings creaking,
Roundabout turning,
Black crows flying across the moon like bats in a horror film.
The creepy voices in the distance make my heart jump.
Empty area full of trees,
Insects walking through the bushes,
But I am still alone,
With the barking dogs.

Stephanie Pittordis (12)
Mount Carmel Technology College

This Is My Poem!

This is my poem,
It was done by me,
I did it myself, obviously.

Whoever reads this poem,
I hope they like it too,
After I read this poem,
I really did, it's true!

I ignored the movements, all the noise
And thoughts about ice cream, friends and toys.
As I just sit there,
Write and rhyme,
It'll soon be over,
Only a matter of time.

Even if I don't win,
I can honestly say,
I am happy and proud,
Of my poem that day.

So this is my poem,
That I wrote today,
Now I can see friends,
Go out and *play!*

Keisha Ekebugo (12)
Mount Carmel Technology College

My Feelings

As I walk through this lonely place,
The floor grabs my feet,
The trees brush my face.

It feels like a dream here,
Tiptoe along the grass,
I'm building up more fear.

The fear is inside me,
Building up even more,
As I get closer,
I look at the floor.
Now . . .
My heart's beating,
Feet racing,
Teeth chattering,
Hairs on end . . .

As I get closer,
It doesn't feel so bad,
As I bend down,
Again I feel sad.

I touch the gravestone,
I get a shiver,
I'm all alone.

Grace Weeden (12)
Mount Carmel Technology College

Atmosphere Poem

Walking through the market,
I can smell fish,
Clean fish,
Salty fish, as salty as the sea.
Walking through the market,
Can hear people shouting,
People who own stalls,
People calling out to their children.
Brushing past people,
Through this busy market,
The sun's warm rays on my back.
Feeling as happy as a baby with candy,
Other people sad,
Hurrying to get home,
Tired, angry, frustrated.
Smell of the wind,
As sweet as cakes,
Straight from the bakery.
Rotten cabbages, fruit,
Other vegetables on the floor,
Awaiting the arrival of the dustbin truck,
To take them to a dirtier place.
The end of the market,
No more stalls,
No more shouting,
No more salty fish,
Or the smell of cakes.
Time to go home,
To a quieter, peaceful, cleaner environment,
Just for me.

Christina Bailey (12)
Mount Carmel Technology College

Atmosphere Poem

Summer has passed
Like the next fashion statement
Look up
The houses
Clouded in faces
They stare at the waves of ice
That cover the fields

I can't move
My roots have frozen
In the sea of white fur
I'm being drawn to the picture
Like a moth to the flame
The ice will drown me
If I take one more step
Into the garden of the Ice Queen

I can taste
The bitter sadness
Of the wind
As it taps me on the shoulder
Pushing me out of its way
The wind prefers to be alone
As he runs around
Bullying and teasing everything
Even the sun.

Abby Mackmurdie (12)
Mount Carmel Technology College

The Wind

Shoves me,
Pushes me against the wall like an old apricot being squashed,
Then hides beneath the hollow trees,
Blowing above me in laughter,
Whoop! He whooshes up my granny's skirt,
Making her dash in laughter,
He pushes the blankets off the line,
Letting it soak in the ground bed.

He nicks the hats but shame they don't match,
Ha, ha, ha, I burst into laughter,
But what can I do, I can't stop it,
It's too strong for me to battle it,
I can't wait till the sun comes out for me to start another rap.

Luz Sanchez Saucedo (12)
Mount Carmel Technology College

Chapel Market

As I am walking through Chapel Market,
The noise grabs me like a hand,
So many people push me like a pram,
The bad smells stick to me like glue,
The nice smells are birds flying and drifting around me,
When I see the McDonald's sign I am dragged in,
The chips slide down my throat softly with ketchup,
Smelly stalls stare at me,
People want to rush and run,
I don't know why,
Suddenly I'm tripping all over the place,
Litter an obstacle in my way,
I have to find a way past,
I love and hate Chapel Market.

Sophie Murphy-Bristow (12)
Mount Carmel Technology College

When It's Raining

The room is dark and warm, just like a cave.
Safe and secure because I'm home.
The thunder is a big, frightening, loud blare,
The rain is like a water hose on full blast.
Pitter-patter of the rain helping me to sleep.
My house is a big, overwhelming, warm blanket,
Protecting me.
Feeling smug and happy because everyone's at home,
Wrapped like a baby,
Nice and cosy,
I'm OK.
Eyelids falling, eyelids drooping,
Eyelids falling,
Eyelids down.

Hannah Akintola (12)
Mount Carmel Technology College

Haunted House

Horrible, terrified, isolated, shivering
I am as white as snow
It's as black as coal in here
It is cold like a freezer and I'm the ice
Woo hoo, ghosts as loud as speakers
Ding-dong, midnight
Terrified with fright like an abandoned child
Skeletons popping up like friends
Chills going up and down my spine
Plant leaves rustling like crisp packets
Someone is there
He is horrendous, no, he is worse
Aaaarrrrrggghhh
Silence is golden in the haunted house
Ha, ha, ha.

Hannah Bailey (12)
Mount Carmel Technology College

Dalston Market

People swarming and swaying,
As if they were snakes,
Sliding through the sand.
It was a wild jungle,
Sky was cloudless,
It was blazing hot,
I felt I was exploring the Sahara Desert.
The sun was killing us.
Fruits were squashed,
Lying there like lifeless souls.
All you see is people,
Running around like rats.
Stalls with multicoloured fruits,
Like the rainbow,
Packed and squashed,
I felt the market was closing in on me.
Half of me smelt the fish,
The other half smelt,
The rich taste of fruits,
It was like they were telling me to come closer.
Dalston market,
Blistering.

Ornelle Kinzenzi Lawu (12)
Mount Carmel Technology College

The Woods

Isolated.
Eerie.
Lonely.
Chilling.
The woods.
Wind howling like a famished wolf,
Tracking down its prey.
Grabbing me.
Hurling me.
Spinning me.
The woods.
Trees.
Bending down.
Trapping me like a prisoner.
Leaves crunching.
Growling like a tiger.
The face in the sky,
Grinning, shining,
Laughing.
The woods.
The woods.
The woods.

Jacky Massaya (12)
Mount Carmel Technology College

Crash

All I see is new faces,
Everything is rush here, rush there.
I'm being pushed everywhere like I'm surrounded with
                                        a sea of people.
Sounds of crying like pain that will never leave all near
                                        departure gates.
Smiles as wide as the ocean, laughter as great as hyenas
                                        near arrival gates.

Waiting, waiting, waiting,
What could it be?
999, I hear as a whisper.
What? I say to myself,
Police, ambulance, fire brigade, sirens mixed together,
Getting louder every second, coming closer.
The area I'm in turns into noise,
All you can hear is screams and crying.
People running everywhere,
Wanting to know
What?
All around me sound of crying and screams
As the people have the news that they have been separated for life
From their loved ones.
The news of a *crash.*

Ayah Omer (12)
Mount Carmel Technology College

The Five Cats

In a house there lived five cats
They all acted like wild rats

The first cat was very thin
Well he liked to watch Rin Tin Tin

The second cat was very fat
And he liked to sit on his owner's lap

The third cat was very tall
That's good for him, his favourite sport was basketball

The fourth cat was very short
He was stupid; he called his paws Neth and North

The fifth cat was very mad
Well he liked to dance; for goodness sake, he owned his
own dancing mat

Now I've told you about the five cats
Told you they were mad, like wild rats

Excuse me, I have to go
I've got some wild cats that I need to adopt

Don't look at me like that
What do you want me to adopt, a wild bat?

Mercy Okech (12)
Mount Carmel Technology College

At The Concert

People queuing up to go in
Like flocks of birds migrating
Inside whistles blowing in my ears
Elephants next to me
Teenagers cheering
Jumping on trampolines
The stage is a sea, spacious and abandoned
I could feel the excitement crawling up my spine
I was right near the stage
And at the back all I could see were ants
Little moving things marching along to the music
Gradually I could feel the tension mounting up
Then suddenly out came some *pop, bangs* and *cracks!*
Then finally the band
Four soldiers, standing tall and straight
At that moment the arena exploded and everyone went mad!
There were girls jumping up and down
Mums falling asleep
There were lights blaring in my face, like I was facing the sun
On the band's faces
I could see their sweat trickling down
Rivers going into the abandoned sea
The arena was a packed suitcase with all of us crammed inside it
But the excitement was all too good to last and soon came the finale
It was great, it was like the millennium all over again!
I screamed until my throat was dry and I had given myself a headache
By the end, everyone had faces on as if someone had died!
When we left, we were like an army of ants, leaving from our nest
I had a great night!

Laurel Fleming (12)
Mount Carmel Technology College

Rush Hour

When morning awakes, stretches and yawns,
When night's sound asleep,
Day taps me on the shoulder,
The alarm speaks and a groan echoes over the city.

Minutes later,
Take a gulp and feel the coffee smooth down my throat,
Like rain trickling down a window,
It's time to go to work.

Car won't start,
The murky coffee stain down the sleeve of my shirt,
Car starts,
Stuck in a jam like a welly in the mud,
Buses packed like red suitcases,
Rush hour's around and he's out to frustrate people.

Inside the train's stomach,
Crammed with people,
No seats, bored and bothered,
Roads are stampedes,
Late for work,
Skirt's creased,
Took a wrong turning,
Horns bleeping,
Clock ticking,
Phone ringing,
Car huffing,
Traffic growing,
Work starting,
Rush hour, king of chaos.

Faye Waddick (12)
Mount Carmel Technology College

Leaves

As I was one long line
Breaking off into small time
As my colour changes
From dark to light
I grow older
With more little lines
In cold winter nights
I'm all alone
As the days pass by
I'm quivering, shaking, freezing
As I fall off my main hold
I get trampled on
Stuck in art books for collages
Then I disintegrate
Back into the earth and dirt of my family
I feel like mist that no one knows
A sufferer of the crackling ice
No one cares about me
Or knows who or what I am
Will you change my life
And tell me who I am?

Julianah Fawehinmi (12)
Mount Carmel Technology College

The Haunted House

Windy, as dark as coal,
Broken windows swaying like dolphins.

Cobwebs knitted perfectly,
Crackly doors making freaky sounds,
Alone in the creepy house.

Spooky pictures giving weird signs,
Long-legged spiders crawling gently on my body

And in no minutes there goes a *bang!*
Eventually the whole house is *haunted!*

Yemisi Soyinka (12)
Mount Carmel Technology College

What A Day!

Crowds of people all around us,
Like a stampeding herd of animals.
People screaming,
Litter everywhere like rats running.
Long queues for the rides,
Like crowds behind a float.
Children wanting candyfloss,
As if they had a sweet tooth.
The sun is beaming in our faces,
Like a light bulb from above.
The sun starts to fall,
As the light bulb darkens.
'What a day!'
We say goodbye.

Bianca-Paige Hylton (12)
Mount Carmel Technology College

What A View

My feet covered in a blanket of sand,
The wind blowing through my hair,
Children building sandcastles,
Cheering cheerfully,
The sea crashing against the rocks,
Like cymbals playing all at once,
Boats skimming the bumpy waves,
Swish, swash,
People anxious to walk the pier,
People anxious to ride the rides,
Me?
I just sit there, like a cat staring out of a window,
Wow, what a view.

Leah Kershaw (12)
Mount Carmel Technology College

Mental Hospital

I'm isolated in this fiery hell,
On the walls there is nothing.
No pictures, no posters, one mirror,
See my reflection,
Look perfectly sane, but not to the doctors.
Patients moan like prisoners and tears sting my eyes like acid.
We wear the same clothes like uniform,
Rock myself and shake like I'm freezing.
Strangers watch me, eyes wide like beasts hunting prey.
Don't think,
Don't eat,
Don't move,
Hardly breathe.
Nurses murmur to each other,
About me,
Like I'm deaf and smile their wicked grins.
Not allowed certain things in my room, in case I try to harm myself,
Have been tempted once or twice.
I cry myself to sleep at night,
I dream of what it's like at home.
I don't want attention,
I don't want sympathy,
I don't want to live.
Sometimes I think that I am going home,
But I forget,
Now this is my home.

Terri McFadzean (12)
Mount Carmel Technology College

The Pub

Through the chipped wood door I enter a dim, smoky room,
Half-filled glasses,
Flat lager,
Crisps scattered everywhere.
I take a seat in the corner,
Keep unnoticed,
As I view the goings on around the room,
Suddenly roars and cheers emerge
From football fans,
Acting like baboons in a jungle-like atmosphere.
Click-clack go the snooker balls,
'Yes, can I help you?'
The barman calls.
As I lean on the sticky beer mats,
I hear a voice,
'Oh what do you think you're doing, Guv'nor?'
Finally the brawl is finished and I can
Enjoy a pub lunch,
Yum, what a lovely bit of food.
Fag ends here,
Fag ends there,
What a mess. Bell rings,
'Last orders please.'
The barman shouts,
Door opens,
Everyone goes out.

Chloe Mitchell (12)
Mount Carmel Technology College

A Summer's Day In The Park

A ball of fire burning your skin,
The sky as blue as the ocean,
Mothers gossiping about the family down the road,
People laughing like hyenas,
The ice cream van plays Sunday morning blues,
Children scatter like mice,
Birds sing along to the latest tunes,
Babies scream as they plea for food,
Dogs bark at their enemies across the field,
Trees spread their holy leaves as they shelter exhausting people,
Brats run to their mummies for money,
Night falls as they escape for home,
To cuddle up in their cosy beds.

Olabisi Oluwa (12)
Mount Carmel Technology College

What Am I?

I fuel passion, hate, love and power
Passing through the hands of every human on Earth
Many times over
Everyone needs, owns and wants me
What am I?

I'm money.

Finn Marr-Heenan (12)
St Mary's CE High School, Hendon

I've Done Nothing Wrong

I walk alone in the night,
Thinking *was I right*
To come all this way
And fight through the day?
I'm in a lot of pain,
As I walk in the rain,
I heavily trudge,
Right through the sludge.

I want to weep,
I am restless from lack of sleep,
I am isolated, on my own,
In the darkness I make my way all alone,
I carry a heavy sack,
On my restless back,
I'm in the cold,
I feel like I've been sold.

Dead people surrounding me,
This is not the way it should be,
It feels like I'm jailed,
Waiting to be bailed,
I've done nothing wrong,
I've done nothing wrong.

Nevena Ivastanin (12)
St Mary's CE High School, Hendon

A Single Touch Of A Hand

Days and nights I'll pray
That I'll find the answer to my cries
That will lead me the way
High up to the sky

Sayings and sayings I will hear from my friends
And this is where it took me
To evil ends
Oh, where else could I be?

A wise man once said:
'A glory of a single hand is a touch'
I stayed in my bed
With my eyes on watch

Those words penetrated my heart
My mind was a whirling spinner
The words showed an art
This could be a winner

My eyes are blinking
My mouth is wide
Why am I winking?
Why can I see a tide?

Out of a shining light
A hand comes out
Is the wise man right?
Why do I have no doubt?

Now I know what I've missed
A single touch of a hand
That would be the top of my list
A single touch of a hand.

Morenike Ariyibi (12)
St Mary's CE High School, Hendon

My Last Time

I am safe, I am in my trench,
No shot can hurt me now,
I will enter the battlefield,
It could be for my last time.

I load my guns,
I act courageous,
An enemy cannon fires,
I am no longer courageous, I am afraid,
I always hear gunshots,
It could be for my last time.

An enemy screams,
He is breathing very badly,
I show no remorse for I am a soldier,
It is my duty to kill,
I have pulled that trigger,
It could be for my last time.

I let more bullets fly,
But so does my enemy,
His last bullet wounds me,
I fall, not knowing if I will ever get back up,
I look around the world,
It could be for my last time.

A sharp stabbing pain,
Blood everywhere,
I look at my friend who is still shooting,
It could be for my last time.

My vision is getting blurry,
I can barely see anything,
My heart is slowing down,
I am dead, everything I did today,
Was for my last time.

Todd Orosco (112)
St Mary's CE High School, Hendon

The Music Maker

I want to make people think
I want to make people feel
I want to make people look inside themselves
And find something they never knew was there before

I want to make people laugh
I want to make people cry
I want to start riots and revolutions

I want to stir people into war
And cajole them into peace

When they hear my music
I want them to pause for thought
To stop and reflect
To become better people

When they hear my music
I want them to be filled with longing

I want them to listen
Really listen

My guitar will never gather dust
Because in it lingers the hopes and dreams
Of a thousand lost souls.

Helen Downer (14)
St Mary's CE High School, Hendon

My Dad

When I heard my dad was going to war
I just wanted to hug him more
I begged him not to go
He said, 'I have to go'
When he left I was scared
Very scared

In his letters he said
'When I get back we can play football'
But without him my day was grey
And he said he had rats in his trench
And he even had bats
His best friend had lost his leg
His name was Greg

When I heard he'd died
I bitterly cried
Never seeing his cheeky smile
Him not reading me a story
Oh, if I could have some glory
It would be my dad back
It would be my dad back

How would you feel if your dad died?
The biggest influence in my life
He was killed by a knife
I want revenge.

Joshua Munn (12)
St Mary's CE High School, Hendon

Distracted Minds/My Sergeant

A wonder, to look up to the man who made me,
Put life in me, a hero for me
Though he's going to be a hero
Now his time has come
'Prove yourself'
Days are cutting short.

He's been gone 3 hours 40 minutes
Fighting, serving for peace
Time's cutting short
He will come back a hero
'My sergeant'.

Days have passed, no letters, no messages
Cold nights by the fire
Me and my mother
Waiting for news to turn up
Time's cutting short
He will be back a hero.

A year has come, time has gone
Maybe something's happened
'No, no, don't be silly he's coming, coming slowly'
I'll wait for him till my time's cut short
My hero will come.

Been so long now, events passed, days gone, now years
Big man now, though I'm still holding on
He's coming one day
Though my days and time are cutting short
My sergeant . . . well?

Imran Mutasa (12)
St Mary's CE High School, Hendon

The Iraqi War

Wars are so tragic,
Everyone always panics.
One day I went to bed,
The next day I find out my friend was dead.
I cried, I cried,
That my friend had died,
He died from being shot in the eye.

I felt extremely sad,
He was the most caring friend I've ever had.
I couldn't believe he'd passed away,
He was very caring was Jay.
Everyone was getting on with the job,
But all I could do was sob.

Oh, that was a funny smell,
It smelt like a poisonous gas shell,
Everyone was rushing to put their gas masks on,
But there was someone in trouble called John,
As his life was coming to an end,
All I could say was, 'You'll soon be on the mend.'

Oh, I feel so alone,
All I want to do is go home.
I said to my captain, 'I need my family.'
He said, 'In this job you didn't do too badly.'

Jeffrey Longdon (12)
St Mary's CE High School, Hendon

The Cynic's National Anthem

I think it's time I taught you
To swallow words with your mind
And spit them out with your tongue

I think it's time I showed you
The difference between sweet fantasy and bitter reality
To explain to you the tang of incarcerated freedom

I think it's time I showed you
The silken web of madness
That binds you and me

I think it's time I told you
Trust isn't the key

For the world halves into groups
Groups are halved by religion
Religions by sects
Sects by sub-sects
Until nothing is left but the individual

And the process starts again
As the individual is halved
By the conscience within.

Ummu-Salma Bashir (14)
St Mary's CE High School, Hendon

Untitled

The ocean swishes and sways,
The sea has very fast waves.
The flower has roots in the grounds,
The grass moves round and round.
The wind blows very hard,
The rain falls in my backyard,
The animals eat and eat,
The humans are very neat.

Katie Pitcher (12)
Skinner's Company's School (Upper)

I Love Moving

Running, jumping, kicking, shouting
Is what I love to do.
Rolling, winding, talking, walking
Are also the best things to do.

Play, whispering, lunging, drinking
Is as good as ice cream.
Laughing, making, drawing, writing
Is like cuddling my cat.

Hugging, dancing, acting, prancing
Is music to my ears.
Locking, climbing, diving, swimming
Is like my baby sister asleep.

Poking, brushing, combing, loading
Makes me jittery.
Moaning, crying, screaming, dying
Hurts so much, I feel like crying.

Jessica Asumang (12)
Skinner's Company's School (Upper)

My Life

My life is like a roller coaster
Going up and down, in and out
I wish once that it would just stop for sixty seconds
Just like a clock that has no power

Life doesn't have a beginning, middle or an end
People might die but their spirit lives on

So I'll just say, 'See you on the other side'
Because life has a meaning
Which is loving, caring
Appreciate someone for who they are
So just think before you say something to someone.

Nicola Smith (12)
Skinner's Company's School (Upper)

My Strange Baby Sister

My baby sister
How can I explain her?
She knows how to get down
But she also can frown
She puts on lipstick
She also puts on Pritt Stick
She moves
She grooves
She bounces
And prances
But most of all, dances
She cries so loud
She acts so proud
She acts all that
She runs like a rat
She makes my life full of commotion
I wish she could swim freely in the ocean
But she is my baby sister
I will always love her so . . .
No, you can't have her!

Sanita Kaur
Skinner's Company's School (Upper)

Dance

Dance is something we do
It is an everyday thing
We dance to the beat of the music
It is like a spirit making me
It is something you cannot explain
It is something to do with movement
That is dance to me.

Jodian Brown (11)
Skinner's Company's School (Upper)

Untitled

I have longed for clean water
And food to keep me alive
People I have seen being killed
Being tortured by the army

I have longed for someone
To be there and save me
I am cold and hungry
And all I've got is the open fields

As I traipse along the sandy ground
My feet are sore and scabbed
My skin is flaking away
Like the snake on its back

I wait to see if anyone
Can rescue me
I pray and sway in the open winds.

Danielle Morgan (13)
Skinner's Company's School (Upper)

Motion

Like walking on water,
Like standing on air,
Like a newborn baby longs to have hair,
Like a ballerina dancing and prancing around,
Like hidden talents longing to be found.
Everyone has to have somewhere to start,
Like that person's idol, admired and proud,
Being watched from a massive crowd.
When that talent finally comes out,
They'll be admired without any doubt
And when that person has succeeded and parted,
They'll always remember where they started.

Frances Poon (11)
Skinner's Company's School (Upper)

Motion In Many Ways

As you step onto the platform,
You are in another world,
You are all dressed up for the party,
As the train moves you see different things,
In the city you don't see many trees and wildlife,
But when you try to see them, they run off,
As soon as you spot some, they run,
They don't stop, they keep on moving
Until they can't see you because they are scared,
Frightened because of the noise, the clutter and bangs of the train,
Then you can't see them anymore,
Which is a shame because you only see stray dogs and cats
With ugly and disgusting rats as well,
Then you suddenly stop,
Stop moving . . . stop hearing the clutter and banging noise,
Then you step out to a world you haven't been,
Like as if it never existed before,
You move out of the train station,
You hear loads of noises like animals protesting
Not to endanger them and kill them,
You have finally reached the club
And you're all dressed up,
Then you step onto the dance floor.

Ade Abdul (11)
Skinner's Company's School (Upper)

Snow

It was a winter's day
The air as bitter as lemon
Wearing my thick fur coat
But still freezing to death
As I trod outside
A whirl of snow came flooding in
I felt like staying in
But yet I had to go to school

Walking in the snow, white all around me
Trying to move another step at a time
Trembling, terrifying, all alone I was
Smash!
In the snow I fell
By myself, no one to help
When I got up, I fell straight back down
No one to help I thought

In the distance I saw a figure
I screamed . . .

Soon after they helped me up
And I said, 'Thank you
Thank you very much'

I went along to school feeling happy and sad.

Camille Daley (11)
Skinner's Company's School (Upper)

Time In Motion

Time in motion,
A bustle and commotion.

A peck at a hard shell, a gasp from an anxious mother,
A beak forcing through an adamant prison
And out ready to face the world,
With a flutter, weak, limp wings,
A baby bird!
The proud mother smiles, oh joyous day!

Time in motion,
A bustle and commotion.

Harboured in the safety of her mother's wing,
The baby bird pioneers, she is learning fast.

Time in motion,
A bustle and commotion.

The baby bird beat her little wings
And bravely flew out of the nest,
A few metres at first,
Then up high above the treetops,
In the lush, pale blue, velvet sky,
The baby bird flew and then she wavered,
She tumbled down out of the sky,
A squeak, a squawk and then a cry,
She tumbled out the sky,
A prowling cat among the grass grinned slyly,
A crimson flood of blood,
A mother bird in awe,
'My baby' she shed a tear.

Time in motion,
A bustle and commotion.

Edanur Yazici (11)
Skinner's Company's School (Upper)

I Travel

I travel around the planet,
Seeking a place to live.
I go from country to country,
Meeting people that still live.
I see these trees,
In the breeze as I walked down a path,
Seeing and hearing some funny laughs.

I travel around the planet,
Seeking a family that loves and does not hate.
I go from place to place,
But no luck comes towards me.
I knock on doors,
I ring bells, but nobody wants me,
So lonely and unloved,
Wishing I was loved.

I travel around the planet,
Seeking a place to work.
Find some money for food and drinks.
It's been 2 weeks since I've had something to eat.
I go around but there's no job for me,
Wishing I had a job.

Zaneb Hussain (11)
Skinner's Company's School (Upper)

The Naughty Wind!

The wind slowly drifts by my face,
The wind rushing around all over the place,
Making people's hair fly around,
Hitting other people's faces as well as their own,
People's hats blowing off their heads,
They are running about like they're mad,
With bags in one hand and the other in the air,
Come on, like that they won't get anywhere!

Amerik Kaur (13)
Skinner's Company's School (Upper)

Lucy's Dance

There was a girl
Her name was Lucy
She was nice but she could be harsh

She had a nice talent
She had a dance
Lucy taught me something
Then she danced away to the music

Oh! I had to learn from her
She was so good
I was jealous of her
I felt broody

Everybody watched her
The crowd cheering for her
I knew I wasn't a part of it
She danced away to the music.

Debbie Shobo (12)
Skinner's Company's School (Upper)

A Born Baby

When my baby brother was a baby,
All he could do was crawl,
But most of all,
He couldn't speak
And he always did leak.

Now he's five
And he's kind of grown up,
Now he can drink from his own cup,
The more he grows,
The more he will know,
But he will forget,
What he did,
When he was a baby.

Haajira Asif (12)
Skinner's Company's School (Upper)

Journey To Heaven

As I stepped onto the plane
I knew I had nothing to gain
Leaving my loved ones
Which I missed tons

The sky roaring with pity
Tears rolled down my cheeks as I arrived in the city
Engines roaring
Rain pouring

My heart told me to stop
But I was nearly at the top
Then seeing the sun
Reminded me of all the fun

The way Granny used to smell
And all the stories she used to tell
But now I was in this big city
With no pity

How I wished to change the time
As my insides tour

I saw bright lightning
And then there was no fighting
I saw all my loved ones and Granny
And I was as happy as a bird

My miserable journey ended
And rewarded me with love
I knew this was not the end
But a beginning of a beautiful life.

Tehmina Shah (13)
Skinner's Company's School (Upper)

My Teacher

My teacher once wore nappies
My teacher used to crawl
My teacher used to cry at night
My teacher used to bawl

My teacher jibber-jabbered
My teacher ran upstairs
My teacher wrote in squiggles
My teacher stood on chairs

My teacher once was naughty
My teacher was so rude
My teacher used a bad word
My teacher spilt her food

My teacher lost her homework
My teacher took too long
My teacher got detention
My teacher did things wrong

My teacher's all grown up now
My teacher can't recall
My teacher thinks she's different
My teacher's not at all.

Blessing Ogunkoya (12)
Skinner's Company's School (Upper)

Change

I don't like change,
I don't like it when we move,
I don't like it when I change school,
I just hate change.

I didn't like it when we moved house,
I didn't like it when my level went down,
I didn't like it when my friend got the crown,
I didn't like it when I left my school,
I didn't like it when I nearly drowned in the pool.

Katie Allin (11)
Skinner's Company's School (Upper)

Imagine

Imagine peace on Earth
No babies dying at their birth
Prisoners out of prison
Happily jumping to do good
Ms Brown teaching children
No shouting or anger
Imagine the Queen Mother risen from the dead
She as a good person indeed
She would come back to life
Wriggling her toes and also her feet
God would rise everyone from death
And all of us dancing to the beat
But what can I say? It can't be done
But if it did happen, we would have fun
But now people are doing their job
Which is to let down their tears
Our own heads and bodies shaking with fear
Imagine freedom and peace
But hear with me, it can't be done.

Sara Lumona (11)
Skinner's Company's School (Upper)

The Man From France

There was a man from France,
Who really, really liked to dance,
He broke the windowpane,
The kitchen was in flames.

He called the firemen,
Then he broke his pen,
After he got his special chain,
Then he ran faster down the lane.

Then he grew a flower,
Which was really full of power,
After all he couldn't explain,
Which was really lame.

Ivy Mensah (11)
Skinner's Company's School (Upper)

Who Can I Tell?

Nothing hurt me more than your behaviour
You gave them a chance to say what they were supposed to say
And you think they are not right
I care about what they say and how they feel but they care not
Because it is not you
And you think it doesn't matter
You took their advice
Did what they told you
Just to make me jealous
I care a lot
But who can I tell?

I cry when I get annoyed
Not because of friends but because of what I have seen
I look up at you
Thinking their words are nothing to you
But words said by fools
You ignore me and go forward to the second mission
It pains me a lot because I care not
Of what people say
Except what you do to me
But who can I tell?

Titilayo Olaifa (14)
Skinner's Company's School (Upper)

Out Of Sight

In the middle of the night
I hold you tight
In the morning light
You're out of sight
I hear a voice inside me
I go to the hospital
They cut my chest
The voice says, 'Not too deep'
They open me up and there you are.

Khadeja Begum (13)
Skinner's Company's School (Lower)

Step By Step

When I was a baby, it was a hard time for me,
But the best thing to eat was cake and cocoa,
When we're babies all we want is love
From Mummy and Daddy.

Now it's time to be a toddler,
All we can say is Mamma and Dada
And so much more,
It's fun because we can crawl, walk
And explore step by step.

Now I'm a child, where we go to school
And rule the hall,
Teachers are like the rough sea.

Now I'm a teenager, where it's a serious matter,
It's now time to eat chocolates and get fatter,
It's time to work hard for exams,
There is no time to have a chat.

Now I'm an adult, where we get married,
Then it's children, like we were before,
Now it's time for work,
What you thought and wished for when you were small.

It's time for old age, where we remember from the past,
It's old age which is last,
But now it's where we die,
But the pleasing thing is where you don't get into any trouble
And no lies,
Now it's time for another life.

Simmeron Kaur (11)
Skinner's Company's School (Lower)

That Special Someone

There he was, I saw him in the street,
I've seen him messy, I've seen him neat.
He was in an embrace with another girl,
I felt hatred for her, I began to swirl.
His brown eyes met the darkness of mine,
With a stare piercing like a lemon or lime.
From his light brown complexion a little lighter than mine,
To his soft-looking cheeks, damn, he's so fine.
It doesn't matter about clothes, age or height,
My love for him soars like a kite.
If you knew him you'd say he was buff,
Cos I know I just can't get enough.
He's caring, my cutie pie, my baby,
Cos he's my teeny, tiny, little teddy.

Teherah Wheeler (13)
Skinner's Company's School (Lower)

Hayley

She started out like any normal baby
She went by the name of Hayley
She soon started to grow
As soon as she could walk she was on the go
Time went so fast
She was out every night
And always home last
She thought she was grown up by the age of 10
Had a boyfriend by the name of Ben
Soon she was a teenager and already on drugs
Started ganging up with all the worst thugs
She was on the street, homeless and no place to go
Wandering around like a lost soul.

Shanel Nassar (13)
Skinner's Company's School (Lower)

Freedom At Night

In a lonely field there; the caravan sits
All lit up with the flowers swaying,
As we drive past to stay.

As we unpack, we smell the fresh air,
All the breeze, as fresh as the sea.
We then sit down for tea
And along come her mates -
All running, as they see the caravan door opening.

The call, 'Mandy! Mandy! We have missed you,
Are you coming out to play?'
'Yes, I'm just getting my jacket
And I will be out.'

Off she goes, running across the field,
As the caravan lights shine and glow,
We see her then we don't,
As she turns a dark corner,
Off she goes.

As time passes by,
We then see her as she walks through the dark field,
All cuddled up with her boyfriend,
As she returns home safe and sound.

Marisa Fleming (14)
Skinner's Company's School (Lower)

Love

My love for you is precious and loving
My love for you is like a rose mixed with honey
My love for you is like a sweet smell of perfume
My love for you is like everything in the world
My love for you is like love for me also
My love is like a dictionary.

Joy Akata (12)
Skinner's Company's School (Lower)

I Wonder

I wonder why the grass is green
And why the wind is never seen?
Who told the birds to make a nest
And told the trees to take a rest?
Creation is as wonderful as beauty and love.

I wonder why the stars shine in the night?
On windy, ferocious nights
It gives me such a fright.
Sometimes I wonder how the trees grow
In such tiny, cute little rows?

When I wonder and ponder of the one who made it,
It makes me think,
The roses are red, the violets are blue,
People made sugar and God made you.

Kimberly Rose (12)
Skinner's Company's School (Lower)

Love

Oh darling boy, how I wish you were mine
When I see you down, looking so cute and perfect
The way you look, the way you smile
I could always faint for your grin

I love you, but do you love me?
My heart is fragile, so don't break it
For I will cry for any broken pieces
Because without them I will be incomplete
So please do me a favour
Don't take a piece of my heart without you in it.

Bukola Olayemi (12)
Skinner's Company's School (Lower)

The Colours Of My Emotions

T he colours of my emotions are so mixed up.
H ere I am with anger and pain.
E veryone thinks that I'm the happiest girl in the universe,
   but do they know the colours of my emotions?

'C ause I just seem so happy, they predict I am.
O h how I cry at night begging everything to be alright.
L ove for my family just turns sour within an hour.
O h how I desire for some happiness in my life.
U nusual taunts I get from my closest friends,
   how I thought they would understand.
R easoning with people to show them my colours of emotions.
S omebody release me out of the cell, please.

O ften, how I think, my life could be much, much better.
F eelings, feelings, nobody understands my feelings.

M y parents are too concerned for other's problems,
   I seem invisible to them.
Y ou can't help me so who can?

E veryone thinks I'm so perfect and lucky,
   but nobody understands.
M y life is just rotating around the clock of life,
   when will it end?
O utraged by the way people think of me,
   can't they see my tears!
T oo many people judge me for what I am
   but do they really know?
I just want somebody to know, to understand,
   a family friend.
O ften I think why can't I just die?
N obody wants to know me or understand me.
S omeone out there please help me.
   Nobody understands the colours of my emotions.

Parminder Rathore (12)
Skinner's Company's School (Lower)

Innocent

What am I doing here?
I haven't done anything wrong
I am innocent
I am not guilty
They're charging me for a case
That's not mine
It's his, not mine
He should be here instead of me
Where is he now?
With his family
Pretending nothing has happened
Spreading rumours about me
Playing innocent
What goes around comes around
I hate him
I wish I never got involved with him
Beloved b*****d.

Temi Atanda (14)
Skinner's Company's School (Lower)

The Flower Of Love

The flower of love
The flower of above
The flower that breathes
The flower that speeds
The flower of love
The flower of above
The flower that smells like the soap Dove
The flower of love
The flower of above
The flower which represents love.

Dulcineia Co' (13)
Skinner's Company's School (Lower)

Seeking Friends . . .

Everybody needs a friend . . .
I need one, you need one, two . . .
Where do I go?
Who do I talk to?
Shall I go looking for someone?
Will someone come looking for you?
They all say making friends is as easy as . . .
How does everyone do it?
Can you show me, make my dream come true?
Do friends think like us?
Must we behave like them?
Should it make a difference?
If it means getting one, or losing one,
There's a lot to consider . . .
Make the right one and never ask
Yourself these questions again.

Zeba Ghanchi (12)
Skinner's Company's School (Lower)

Lovely Birds!

Quack!
Nice birds singing nice songs, quack!
Hopping here and there, quack!
Flapping their beautiful wings,
Moving very fast in the sky,
I sit and wonder, how and why these are done,
Can someone tell me why all these are done?
Maybe to worship God?
Maybe to praise God?
I guess all is done in the name of creation.

Samira Adotey (11)
Skinner's Company's School (Lower)

Untitled

The night watched, as he crept through the glade,
The wind blew through the trees, clutching at him with icy blades,
The man went on, gazing into the dark with his hawk-like eyes,
Owls came at him, striking his eyes with sharp talons,
But still he went on,
Wild cats ravaged him, drawing crimson blood with razor edge claws,
But he still strode on,
Banshees screeched at him, deafening him with
                                blood-shattering cries,
But he still carried on,
The man went on, ignoring all attempts to hinder him,
He went on, desperate to attain his goal, ignoring his life ebbing away,
He came to the pool, the pale goddess of the sky
                                reflected in the depths,
He smiled, a smile full of anguish and plunged to his doom,
Deep in the endless lagoon, he died,
His soul joining his kin of the stars.

Imogen Armstrong (14)
Skinner's Company's School (Lower)

Mother And Daughter

Mother and daughter are just like best friends,
Playing, laughing and joking around,
They are too close, they are best pals,
They never can have a row.

In the future, maybe they will
Have a row, a very bad row,
They could kill, they could harm,
They could do something you may not know.

Mother and daughter will still be best friends,
They will come back and joke around again,
They will still be close and be best pals,
But maybe have another row.

Harkesh Kaur (12)
Skinner's Company's School (Lower)

Romantic Day

When I see his eyes, I can almost plead for his love,
My heart pounds every second
And it's getting stronger and unbreakable,
When will he know and when will he not know?
I know he will know soon.

I jump around and shout around
For him to know I love him so,
But deep inside I know he feels the same way too,
My love for you is so strong,
I can't keep it any longer,
My love for you will never end,
You will always be mine,
Now and for evermore.

I can love you in a mist and you will never know,
But for now I will, I will keep it to myself.

Aminata Fofana (12)
Skinner's Company's School (Lower)

The Day I Lost My Mum

I cried, I cried,
I could cry no more,
I thought to myself, *why did she have to go?*
I see her image in my eyes,
Like an angel from the sky.
I say to myself, come back to my eyes,
But she never comes by,
I wonder, did she really love me
Or was it just an illusion?
One, two, three, four,
She isn't coming back anymore.

Stephanie Baynes (12)
Skinner's Company's School (Lower)

Anger Is . . .

Anger is thunder piercing the heart full of love,
Anger is not below or not above,
Anger is when you feel you've been shoved,
Anger is the feeling of a forever trapped dove,
Anger is . . .

Anger is when you have been stabbed with a knife,
Anger is the feeling when somebody has destroyed someone's life,
Anger is frustration and strife,
Anger is a betrayed and angry wife,
Anger is . . .

Anger is me getting my teeth,
Anger is when I feel like stamping my feet,
Anger is my uncontrollable hands,
Anger is when my mum reprimands,
Anger is . . .

Anger is the Devil's work,
Anger is present were the Devil lurks,
Anger is what God tries to stop,
Anger is what leads you to the cops.

Even when there's anger, you best keep out,
'Cause that's what this poem is all about.

Shaziya Amad (14)
Skinner's Company's School (Lower)

When She Left

When she left, I was lonely again
When she left, smiles turned into sulks
When she left, the sun started crying once again
When she left, the tears that came out of my eyes were pure
All I needed was the loneliness cure.

Sara Qureshi (13)
Skinner's Company's School (Lower)

How Can I Go On?

How can I go on,
Living day to day,
Working day to day,
In this terrible life?

He beats me,
He rapes me,
I even saw him kill another man.
This other man was my brother,
My brother. The son of my mother,
The grandson of my grandmother.

But don't get me wrong,
Life was once before sweet.
All you could feel every day was the heat,
But then things went wrong.

Before I started working for him,
I went through things you couldn't imagine.
Could you survive?
If I didn't survive,
I wouldn't be writing this.

I said to myself one day,
Don't give up,
Things could get better,
But I was lying to myself.

Tomorrow I am fifteen,
I have no mother,
No brother,
No father.
But how can I go on,
Living day to day,
Working for him,
Being his wife?

Abena Bruwaa Adjei (13)
Skinner's Company's School (Lower)

The Way I Feel

I feel left out from somewhere,
I feel like no one cares,
I feel my family is away,
I have just one more day.

I feel like a dead plant,
I wish I could do something, but I just can't,
I feel so bored, everyone is driving a Ford.

I feel so sad,
Everyone has gone bad.

I feel poor on the outside,
I just want to hide.
I feel no one is there for me,
All that makes me happy is the deep blue sea.

Alexis Aryeetey (13)
Skinner's Company's School (Lower)

My Father

My father,
   My guide,
      My strength,
         My friend.

There in times of need,
Even when I offend,
He dries my tears,
When I cry in bed.

He is
   My father,
      My guide,
         My strength,
            My friend.

Maria Ayodabo (13)
Skinner's Company's School (Lower)

My Life

My life is like paradise
It's precious
Peaceful
And very fresh

I have my family
I have my friends
I have the rest of my life to rest

I'm in paradise
Not in Hell
I'm having fun
Eating my bun

I love my family
I love my friends
I love to see my family friends

I'm not a girl
Not yet a woman
All I need is time
At the moment that is mine
While I'm in-between.

Anisa Halimah Ahmad (11)
Skinner's Company's School (Lower)

Eternity

E very time I see you
T ears will come down
E very hour I will be missing you
R un away with my love
N asty, sweet thing, but you're still mine forever
I mportant to love me
T rust and friendship
Y ou and me are lovers forever.

Selmin Alptekin (13)
Skinner's Company's School (Lower)

Jealousy Is . . .

Jealousy is when your palms get sweaty,
Jealousy is when you're overwhelmed with self-pity,
Jealousy is my brain in confetti
Jealousy is . . .

Jealousy is eyes that are green,
Jealousy is something that makes you mean,
Jealousy is more when you're a teen,
Jealousy is . . .

Jealousy is protective,
Jealousy is possessive,
Jealousy is something that makes you active,
Jealousy is . . .

Jealousy is a violent explosion,
Jealousy is a deep, deep emotion,
Jealousy is a brain disillusion,
Jealousy is . . .

Farzana Akhtar (13)
Skinner's Company's School (Lower)

Dolphins

D olphins are calm creatures,
O h how they are beautiful,
L ovely, loopy mammals they are,
P recious to the universe dolphins are,
H ave some respect and stop killing them,
I n the ocean, they are so amazing,
N ever in my life have I seen a dolphin so nice,
S o when you see a dolphin remember never to harm it.

Nazli Kurtulmus (12)
Skinner's Company's School (Lower)

Jobs

What would it be like to be someone else?
Well, let's see.
Would I like to be the person
Or would I like to be me?

Would I like to be a singer
And go on tour?
And when I leave the fans
They'd scream for more.

Would I like to be a traveller
And travel the whole world?
And when I'm in Australia,
I'd meet an Australian girl.

Would I like to be a doctor
And perform operations?
Nah,
There'd be too many complications!

Would I like to be a lawyer
And rest a case?
And stand in court
With a straight face?

All these jobs sound really great
And maybe I might choose one, one day!

Charelle Samuels (12)
Skinner's Company's School (Lower)

What's Love And Peace?

Love is . . .
Love is wonderful
Love is happiness
That will
Give you
Joy
Love is when someone
Cares for you
So you know someone
There is waiting
For you

Peace is . . .
Peace is quiet
Peace is no problems
Just joy in your life
Peace is lovely
Fresh flowers
And treats.

Shola Judun (11)
Skinner's Company's School (Lower)

The Shining Night Sky

The sky has many stars
Always shining down
Putting light upon the land
Brightening up every town

All of us look the same from way up high
Imagine if someone is watching
Somewhere in the sky

Loads of us, loads to see
Looking at all of us, looking at me

If you were to fly up in the deep blue sky
What would you think of us down there?
Would you even bother? Would you even care?

Jennifer Starling (11)
Skinner's Company's School (Lower)

Death

I sat down,
With fear written all over me.
A scene drops into my mind,
Like a dark cloud,
Getting ready for a storm.
Lightning crashes
And that's when I see,
My grandad die.

I run to the phone,
Dialling,
A lady with a calm voice
Says, 'Connection was lost,
Please try again later.'
I throw the phone in rage,
Like a small, hard ball.
I sit down crying,
I could have made an ocean,
Bigger than the Pacific,
With my salty, dark blue tears.
Then someone taps me
On my shoulder . . .

I find my mum,
Smiling at me
And I see the shining sun,
Peeking through my window,
Then I notice it had all been
A nightmare. An awful one.

Selin Kavlak (11)
Skinner's Company's School (Lower)

Junk Food

Crisps, sweets
All you can eat
When I look at them
It makes my heart beat
Chocolates, lollipops
I just can't stop
Someday my ears are going to pop.
Get £5 to buy some sweets,
Start at the café at 'all you can eat',
Bubblegum, I want some,
So I can put it in my tum,
I'm getting fat,
Now how about that,
I can't get up from where I'm sat!

Joannie-Lee Harris (11)
Skinner's Company's School (Lower)

Mondays!

Mondays, Mondays,
I hate those Mondays,
It rains like lightning
And dries like wind.
Every time it's Monday,
I feel so lonesome.
As I walk down the street,
I get a tear in my eye.
People stare like I'm an alien,
That just landed on Earth.
Tuesdays, Wednesdays, Thursdays,
Fridays, Saturdays and Sundays,
Oh yes, I'm so happy,
But then comes Monday,
Oh no, oh no!

Anne-Marie Moses (13)
Skinner's Company's School (Lower)

Spaghetti

Spaghetti! My favourite!
All wormy and wriggly
Slippery and slimy
Slurpy and sloppy
That's how I like it

Mincemeat! My favourite!
All chewed and tatty
Juicy and succulent
Lots of bits everywhere
That's how I like it

Splat! Double splat!
It tastes so good
The wormy spaghetti and tatty mince
Chew, chew, chew
Gulp, gulp, gulp
Splat! Splat!

That was delicious!
Burp!
Pardon me!
Well I'd better clear off before Mum finds me
Up the stairs I go, as quick as a flash
Made it! I'm in my room!
Sana!
Uh-oh!

Sana Ahmed (11)
Skinner's Company's School (Lower)

Why Did You Hurt The Black People?

A world full of people,
White is not the only colour,
There is another,
A special one too!

If a black person fell right beside you,
Would you help them back up
Or would you be racist and disrespectful?
They would not like it . . . would you?

Imagine a world full of people different from you
And you are ashamed,
People throw dirt at you
And you have no control.

That's how the blacks were treated,
But would it happen again, but to the white?
They would not like it,
Whipped for no reason.

Answer me one question,
Why did you hurt the black people?

Isabel David (13)
Skinner's Company's School (Lower)

Relationships

You can have a relationship through a mother
A relationship through a father
The meaning of a relationship is all to stick together

To love
To care
Almost anywhere
Your mum, your dad
Are always there to prepare.

Serap Cifci (13)
Skinner's Company's School (Lower)

I Want It

It's pink and fluffy,
Sugary and yummy!
I lick my lips just looking at it,
'I want it!'
As you know I always win
And enjoy gobbling it up!
The next one, it's round and red,
Sticky and juicy, there are more,
But I like this one and *'I want it.'*
I really like the colour green,
It's green, round, picked off a tree
And waiting for me, because *'I want it.'*
What's that I see lurking behind those boxes?
A turtle?
With its brownish shell and cute face,
'I want it!'
Ooh, I like the teddy that girl's holding,
I wonder if Dad will buy me that teddy?
Its furry smooth skin,
Black eyes, small nose, it's perfect just for me,
'I want it!'

Yeliz Yesilyurt (12)
Skinner's Company's School (Lower)

Love!

Love is a beautiful feeling,
It can hurt and it's what you can't stop thinking of,
It feels as if your heart is melting like butter,
It feels as if your heart just missed a beat,
It can burn your heart like fire,
There are many types of love,
It can be hard,
It can be easy,
But that's the way true love is!

Faiza Asif (14)
Skinner's Company's School (Lower)

Untitled

No matter where you look,
No matter where you go,
You will never find someone
The same as you.

Some white, some black,
They could even be blue
And it shouldn't really
Matter to you.

Some short, some tall,
Some big, some small,
Everyone has different eyes,
Everyone has a different nose,
Everyone can strike a different pose.

When we smile, you can plainly see,
There is something hidden inside me,
It could be good,
It could be bad,
But soon I will be glad.

I'm happy it's a good thing
And not a bad thing
That means I will be glad.

Danni Lansdowne (13)
Skinner's Company's School (Lower)

Gold

Flowers will die,
The sun will set,
But you're a friend,
I won't forget.
Your name is so precious,
It will never grow old,
It's engraved in my heart,
With letters of *gold!*

Sonia Kaur Lohia (12)
Skinner's Company's School (Lower)

What Is English? What Is Yoruba?

English,
We speak it, we live it,
Those foreign people think it's 'a hit'
They would laugh if we fell in a pit
Do we have to be so serious?
Too much English makes me delirious
They are nice people are they not?
Or maybe I have lost the plot!

Yoruba,
I speak Yoruba,
I use it to joke around,
I use it to be serious,
when I speak a sentence to my mum,
She thinks I'm a genius,
If I was to speak it to myself,
It would be meaningless,
We are humans too, we all have fear in us!

English makes sense,
Yoruba is no different,
But if we put it together 'hence'
'Mó fé go to ilé of my friend.'
See, no sense,
When I'm put on the spot to speak it,
I find an excuse, in an instant.

Esther Areola (13)
Skinner's Company's School (Lower)

A Scary Winter Night

One cold winter night I sat in my bedroom,
I suddenly heard a strange noise, *bang, bang!*
It was like a sound of a drum,
I glanced out beyond the window.

When I looked at the sky, I saw,
The clouds running like a river,
The stairs were blinking like my glitter hairspray.

Oh my god, was it only my imagination
Or was this really happening?
I rushed to the bathroom and dipped
My head into a bucket of water.
I just wanted to make sure I wasn't
Imagining things.

But guess what? This was one
Unforgettable winter's night.

Sharmela Parchment (14)
Skinner's Company's School (Lower)

Fear . . .

Fear is blackness in the dark
Fear is something that leaves a mark
Its shadows roaming in your room
It's a stain inside you, fear is your doom

Fear is something that makes you run
Fear is being struck by a gun
Not recognising the horror that lies ahead
Being twitchy and spotting nothing but red

Seeing blood pouring out . . .
In a place, where you're filled with doubt
Staring at the pain within those dark eyes
Feeling so useless, as if you're going to die.

Yumna Ahmed (14)
Skinner's Company's School (Lower)

Oh No!

I'm running fast in the right track,
The butcher's there shouting, 'Come back!'
I got bread for tea and milk for Mum,
She's going to be so happy with what I've done.

In my uniform I'm running free,
Lots of people looking at me,
The wind's blowing my face and hair,
I can see my house very clear.

Just a few steps I'm nearly there,
As Mum comes out the door right here,
'Oh no, dear, I forgot the butter.'
Just quickly run, 'Oh no' I did mutter.

I come from the shop and forget to pay,
I hear them shouting, 'Come back this day . . .'
Again I'm running in the right track,
Still I can hear them saying, 'Come back . . .'

I'm coming home tired and down,
I'm sweating, tired, I've got a frown,
I'm at home, I've got homework,
After then I can play and lark.

I reach in my bag for a lollipop,
Oh no, I've left it in the shop,
I'm lying down, tired and sad,
Silly fool, angry and mad.

Now I remember my teacher saying:
'Everybody, the whole class please you better pay attention . . .
Because if this work is not done, you're going to get . . .
Detention!'

Latisha Marius-Palmer (11)
Skinner's Company's School (Lower)

My Family

Mum calling me
Mum annoying me
Telling me to do stuff
Well, I'm chuffed

My dad gives me everything
Everything even *bling blings!*
My sister saying, 'Spoilt brat'
And I give her a little pat
Don't worry 'cause you're the odd one out

Sisters, sisters, sisters
Fighting, biting, punching
Obey my rules or I'll beat you up
Beat me up, I'll hammer you down

Joking about with my brother
Having fun
Listening to my problems
It doesn't bother him, because he's my best brother
And my only brother

Cousins, talking, playing, having a laugh
Screaming, shouting
Leaving echoes and paths
Looking back on what we've done together
Those times were the best ever.

Nana Ababio Duncan (11)
Skinner's Company's School (Lower)

Love

Love is like a shiny sun in a cold winter
Love is like a garden of red roses
Love is like a holy story for a lover
Love is the best thing for lovers
When someone falls in love,
She/he cannot accept whether it is right or wrong
This shows that you love each other
And you cannot see the problems
Love is a beautiful thing if you know
That you are doing a right thing
And you are choosing a right person
If you really love someone
It means that you should stay with that person forever and ever
Unless one of you dies
Briefly I can say that you can only stay alive
If you are in love.

Sadaf Zolfaghari (14)
Skinner's Company's School (Lower)

Stand Your Ground, Fight Back!

When bullies come to bully you
Do not walk away
It'll only make it worse
Say what you have to say
They should call you whatever
'Cause you should say what's on your mind
Guess it's easier for them to swallow
If you sat and cried
'Cause when a victim fires back
Then suddenly the bully don't know how to act
So they'll do what little siblings would do
Blame that you started it all the way through
So now you know if they say you suck
Go and pound them 'cause it's their tough luck.

Senem Aysan (12)
Skinner's Company's School (Lower)

If I Could Have

If I had a puppy, I would name him Skilla
If I had a brother his name would be Junior Miller
If I had a friend her name would be Mandy
We would go to somewhere quiet, sunny and sandy

If I had a car I would like a Renault Megane
If I could go on holiday I'd take a trip to Japan
I'd take Mummy, Daddy and sister Joanne
Go to the beach and get a tan

If I was a few years older I'd start my career
In the singing industry like Madonna or Cher
If I had a boyfriend he would buy me a teddy bear
Which I would hug, snuggle and take everywhere

If I could get married I'd wear a big white dress
My husband, my hero would have to look his best
If I end up with children, I'd like 2 boys and a girl
My husband and children would be everything in my world.

Haley Jackson & Kisela Tunani (14)
Skinner's Company's School (Lower)

The Moonlight

Every night when I go to sleep,
I see a shining light in the sky,
When I look at it, all I can see is an eye,
It was a face in the moonlight,
That smiles every night.

Right now I'm very sad,
But last night I was very mad.
As I look out the window all I see is a bright, round moon
Just like a cashew nut.
I feel like flying in the sky and going far away
Where I can be very happy.

Neslihan Demirci (13)
Skinner's Company's School (Lower)

School

School is boring
I have to get up early in the morning
I have to get an education
But while I'm there, I just lose my concentration

Lessons always seem to go on forever
The teachers always tell us that we will be clever
Finally break time comes
But then we've got another lesson to learn our sums
Teachers never stop talking
So we get bored and they tell us to start walking

Lunchtime's here
But then we have to eat and get ourselves back into gear
All I want to do is please my mum
So why do I always have to spit out my gum
Everyone waits for the bell to ring
When it finally comes, you feel you want to sing
When the next morning comes, you just want to drop dead
All we just want to do is lie in our bed.

Stephanie Healy (14)
Skinner's Company's School (Lower)

Summer

Summer is the happiest time of the year,
Long sunny days with nothing to fear.
It's time for picnics, swimming and hikes,
For eating ice cream and riding our bikes.

We can pitch out tents and sleep outdoors,
Or visit the seas on distant shores,
Winter is over, we all feel happy,
Summer is here, it's holiday time.

Khadijah Suleman (13)
Skinner's Company's School (Lower)

Black Woman Rise

In the death of her silence solitude she rose
She heard the shot when Yaa-Asantewaa fired her gun
While her infant was strapped to her back
In a cloth barely enough to cover her hips
She saw when Hariet led the slaves to the underground
She saw the truth when Sojouner provoked justice

She walked on the Sahara, tracing
The footsteps of her lost children
She heard when Kilimanjaro echoed
The cries of her stolen children

She cradled kings' infants
When they asked for their daddy
She heard when they said Klinnie had
Become a fallen woman

She fed the starving Ethiopian
And rocked the orphaned
Ugandan to sleep while
AIDS rained upon the continent

She is the houchie mama
Who houched from pimp to pimp
On the street of Harlem
To put food on her children's plate

She screamed when the body bag at morgue
Revealed the face of her son
The roll of thunder heard not her cries
While the rainbow was not enough and the
Unmerciful cloud rained unto her cheap
Mascara to her payless shoes

She read when Halle got her Oscar
She saw when J-Lo was awarded
The benefit of what should have been hers
She read when Beyoncé
Bounced her acclaim bump
And became the commodity
Of the twenty-first century

She rose out of the concrete
She travelled from Sahara to Georgia
She is the most knowledgeable
Most educated, most persecuted
She struggles through centuries
Arise!
She is no other than a black woman.

Juliet Gifty Owusu (14)
Skinner's Company's School (Lower)

I Hear . . .

I hear the cry of the children,
I hear the pain of the people,
I hear the emotions through the wind,
I hear the sorrow.

Then I hear . . .

I hear the joy of children,
I hear the love of people,
I hear the laughter through the wind,
I hear the happiness!

Toni McGregor (14)
Skinner's Company's School (Lower)

Emotions

I'm sitting there thinking about the times I was with you
And all those times I cried with you
Feeling sorry for not having told you
How much I loved you
And how much I still do
Think about the days we were together
I cry at night when you're not there
I try to smile but the pain is too much
I miss you too much to let you go.

Noemi Nicolau (14)
Skinner's Company's School (Lower)

Eyes

I can see you walking by,
I can see you, even if I blink my eye.

You crossed the road,
I moaned
And ran through the road like a toad.

My eyes were looking at you sigh,
So I didn't see a moped coming by.

I hit my head on the moped,
I saw red, I felt like I was tied in bed.

My eyes changed black,
I tried to turn back.

I felt so weak,
It was like my head had a bloody leak.

Now I can't see you walking by,
Now I can't see you, even if I blink my eye.

Tulin Ukuser (13)
Skinner's Company's School (Lower)

Count 1 To 3

I'm all alone in the dark
Standing by myself in the park
Seeing the car lights
Shining so bright
Like stars in the sky
Owls looking at me so shy
Owling away, making me stay away
Birds flying tree to tree
Counting 1, 2, 3
Go away! Go away!
Come back another day.

Reena Kaur (13)
Skinner's Company's School (Lower)

Women . . .

Women are the best
Women don't mess
Women are strong
And know when they are wrong

Women are sometimes right
Women hate to fight
Women like to cook
Some hate reading books

Women get high with men
And go out with men called Ben
Women are tall, as high as a wall

Women are sometimes weak
And think men are freaks
Women like to shop, until they drop

Women like to spend money and call people honey
Women think make-up is good
And eat food when they are in the mood

Women never stink and like to wear pink
Women are tight and go out at night
Women are humble and hate to mumble

Women are dry and once in a while they cry
Women tend to pay the bill and are sometimes on a pill
Women are like thunder and like to surrender.

Fazila Boodi (14)
Skinner's Company's School (Lower)

The One

The one, who I've desired for oh so long,
Watching him day by day,
Through April and May.
I'm getting impatient now,
Like a hungry dog, but I'm hungry for his love,
My heart is beating faster, like bongo drums.

Finally one day, I got brave,
Day by day, I crave,
For the boy I desire.
I saw his face,
My heart started to race.

I opened my mouth but,
The words wouldn't come out,
I was about to shout,
When he said, 'I really like you.'

When I heard these words,
My whole world turned upside down,
It was as if I wanted to dance,
But I was too embarrassed.

He took my hand,
Although it was sweating,
My heart was begging,
For him to stop because
I felt so weak.

His eyes were sparkling like stars,
I felt like he was my Milky Bar,
Sweet and cute,
Loving and caring,
Finally the one, is my one.

Burcu Karamahmutoglu (13)
Skinner's Company's School (Lower)

I Love You

I love you,
I hate you, those are the words wondering
around in my head, lost, trying to find a
place to settle and be stable.
Wondering why I had fallen for a guy like you,
maybe it was your smile that had me feeling
funny inside, like a schoolgirl having a crush
on her 8th grade teacher.
Your eyes were bright and would sparkle
whenever they made four with mine, like the
moon being reflected off the ocean in the night.
I love you for making me fall in love with you,
I hate you because you're always making me blue.
My heart and my mind is fighting to make the
thoughts going through my head stable.
Like two boxers in a boxing ring fighting for the
championship, 'Yes, yes, you're the one' my mind says.
'No, I can find another one,' my heart is shouting!
I wish I could see you, but I wish I had never
met you, why did I ever lay eyes on you?
Why did you approach me and say 'Hi,'
why didn't he ask for directions and
say 'Goodbye'?
I still don't know what to do, with all these
emotions passing through, but in the end I
keep on hearing I love you and I hate you.

Ruchelle Lee (16)
Skinner's Company's School (Lower)

Love . . .

Love, what is love?
Love is sweet, love sour.
Love makes you happy, love makes you sad,
Love makes you feel free, like a bird in the sky.
Love is beautiful, like a rainbow,
Love is a breath of fresh air.
Love makes you feel strong, sometimes weak,
Love, the touch of love is so sweet.
Love is like fire,
Love is like the stars shining in the sky,
Love brings peace and war,
Love makes you feel good about yourself,
Love, the greatest love is when someone loves you back.

Tashanno Robinson (13)
Skinner's Company's School (Lower)

Love

L aughter
O pen
V alentine
E motion

Roses are read
Violets are blue
If I were a moon
I'd split myself in two
I'd give the dark to people
And leave the light for you

Love is like glass
Handle it with care
Once it's broken
It's hard to repair.

Ayesha Shaikh (13)
Skinner's Company's School (Lower)

Poetry In Motion

My mother,
My provider,
My friend,
My guidance.

That's always beside me,
Whenever I need her,
She's loving, she's caring,
She can be tough and strict,
But all I know is, she is my mother.

Dami Beckley (13)
Skinner's Company's School (Lower)

Hearts Comforts

Crying in the corner,
Wiping her tears, the mourner,
Pathetic expressions show,
Her heart wants to follow,
For her love is under flora,
She runs in vain,
Trying to find her sanctuary,
Nothing more to comfort her,
But pain and misery!

Jessie Callender (13)
Skinner's Company's School (Lower)

Cold The Colour Of Ice

Cool the colour of rain
Warm the colour of a flowing stream
Hot the colour of coffee
Temperature the colour of a rainbow.

Sanjaya Dewan (12)
The Compton School

Feelings, You Are Who You Are!

The light and tender stench of *hate,*
Fills the room.
Whilst the vicious aroma of *love,*
Remains in your heart.

The glaring look in someone's face,
Tells you how they feel.
A blissful smile,
Is just as much as respect!
The smirking face,
Tells you their trouble.
But deep inside the heart is supple.
Squashy.
Malleable,
Look inside to see the *real* person,
Maybe you'll discover something.
Have admiration and adore the skin you're in.

You're not luminous or gleaming,
But '*You Are Who You Are!*'

Munim Islam (12)
The Compton School

Cold The Colour Of Ice

Cold the colour of ice,
Sky all grey and dull.
The ground so hard and covered in snow,
Crunching beneath my feet.
Snowstorms gathering in the sky,
Ready to come down on you and I.
As the snow comes down,
Children's laughter fills the town.
Crisp white ground looking like a fresh page,
Children playing whatever their age.
As the children begin to tire,
They head inside to snuggle up by the cosy fire.

Bethany Palmer (11)
The Compton School

My Dream Land

Every night I go there
Not a night goes by
I see the things I want to see
While I'm frozen in time

I see my hopes and dreams
Before my very eyes
Sometimes when I fall over
I need not start to cry

Because when I'm in my dream land
Nothing can hurt me there
I feel nothing but happiness
While I float in the air

But soon the dream goes murky
And things begin to fade
And soon I start to fall down
Hoping to be saved

But the more I start to struggle
The faster I shall fall
And soon I lay awake in bed
And my dream I can't recall.

Melda Kazim (12)
The Compton School

Cold The Colour Of Ice

Cold the colour of ice
Wind as strong as a grappling bear
Rain freezes before it even forms
Even polar bears stand frozen.

Snow freezes the second it hits the ground
No penguin can swim the waters
No Eskimo can climb the mountains
No jacket can protect you for it is
Cold the colour of ice.

Emiliano Rodriguez (11)
The Compton School

Britain For Me!

Cold, freezing, that's Britain,
Heavy traffic in London.
Fields of corn in the country
The smell of pollution and flowers.
The lovely old buildings full of history,
The sound of animals and home.
People from all over the world, Asia, Africa,
South America, North America, Europe and Oceania.
Languages are plenty,
Friendships are many.
The English traditional food, fish and chips,
Now there are many others like kebab shops, Indians and Chinese
And many more.
The Public Services are not really good,
But because of the NHS we all get free hospital attention.
School is a law in here, you must attend.
You also do not pay for school.
All the services are free of charge.
You only pay taxes,
And that's Britain for *me*.

Afshin Yazdi (13)
The Compton School

Cold The Colour Of Ice

Cold the colour of ice, the snow falling hard like rocks from the sky,
Teeth chattering, because it's too cold.
Arm gone dead because of no heat.
Heaters on full power which should crumble and shatter the stones.
Houses feel like icicles beginning to crumble on you,
Heat really strong.
Barely able to hold the coldness.
Drops begging to come through.
Suddenly ice breaks through like a building to collapse on you.
Things are as cold as ice, are you too?

Hiran Amba (11)
The Compton School

The British Life Day By Day . . .

As I look around the globe, I see many cultures.
Religions mixed together, but none as much as a tiny
island in Europe.
The green painted landscape and the transparent blue
sea around.
The sky thick with clouds.
Flash forward a few years and the scene has totally changed.
Men in golden helmets and elegant metal armour, travelling
on roads, laid with tar.
A few more years ahead and many reigns of kings and queens
will pass, many conquerors, philosophers and scientists
have now changed the world.
Now come back to the present and just look around you,
the changes are extreme.
Dull grey streets, lit by dim yellow street lights and houses
boxed together, labelled and arranged.
Always expecting some excitement,
that you know will never come,
Day by day
by day . . .

Parimal Depala (13)
The Compton School

Cold The Colour Of Ice

Cold the colour of ice
The feeling has its own device
Blue the colour of the sea and sky
Oh what pleasure to the eye
Yellow the colour of the sun
The first thing we think of is fun
Green the colour of our fields
For here our heart yields
All year round these things are here to lend
But cold the colour of ice
Will always be from beginning to end.

Shivan Vaya (11)
The Compton School

Autumn's Child

The zephyr of an incoming winter,
The seldom gust of a leaving autumn,
The size of a golden birth,
Into the flurry of golden leaves,
A child is born.

The golden amber landscape,
Of a more picturesque shape,
A glaze of perfection,
A never-ending love,
From a child of pure life and justice,
Life of a child of gold,
Can never be sold.
Except,
It can't escape the winter cold.

The snow has returned,
The cold has settled,
And the autumn's child is no more,
The white of a winter blizzard,
The chill of a frosty ghost,
The shrill scream of the windy killer,
The autumn child of amber glaze,
Has died,
And the season is buried under the snow,
Along with autumn's child.

Sam Mustafa (13)
The Compton School

Class 7M

Blend the children altogether
add a little work
sprinkle on a pinch of laughter
then let them set . . .

Chop a little Spanish
slice a little English
grate a bit of maths
add a drop of science
then stir while adding history
blend them with some homework
then set in the oven for six years . . .

Take them out and wait to see what they will be
to top it off,
add, some art that's all been grinded nicely
then leave it on a teacher tray
and check them every lesson . . .

If still uncooked
turn up the heat and wait in excitement
then eat your heart out and enjoy
because you have a treat from heaven . . .

Warning
Take care of with loving care
and treat them all the same
or blended flavour teacher icing
will get you.

Bryony Willis (11)
The Compton School

Looking Smart

Looking smart,
Looking neat, blazer on
Black shoes on feet,
Shirt tucked in,
Tie six feet long
Hat, coat or gloves
That's wrong, wrong, wrong.
Jewellery, piercings
Mostly forbidden,
Here's a huge plaster
Make sure it's hidden.
Apart from that
What you wear is your choice
But socks must be dark,
Thanks girls and boys.

Looking smart
Baggy shirt,
Worn in trousers
What's a little dirt?
You're happy with
Your clothes, you're
Different to the rest
Don't care what people think,
In your mind
You're the best.
Converse, Etnies, Vans
You name it, if you have the money
Go ahead and claim it.
Top it all with a dangling belt now,
Off to your gig, go
Drink to your health.

Looking smart,
Denim and tracksuit,
Dyed blonde hair and gold rings to match.
Nike, Nickelson, Evisu, Schott,
As long as it's a label
You're the best of the lot.

Burberry hat, Burberry scarf,
Burberry everything
No one will laugh.
Trousers rolled up
Gold earrings in
Now off to the park
Make sure you look thin.

The definition of smart,
There isn't just one
So wear what you like,
Believe me it's more fun.

Jamie Demetriou (15)
The Compton School

Cold The Colour Of Ice

Cold the colour of ice
I see it in his eyes,
he ventures forth
the water deep
to catch a big surprise.

Stalking, watching, moving,
slow,
we see no footprints in the
snow.

His coat so fiery,
dense and thick,
his eyes do smoulder
his mouth is slick.

Gracefully as time goes by,
he pounces harsh
his prey does die,
meal tonight will be a feast
King of the Jungle
'this elegant beast'.

Marcus Cara (12)
The Compton School

Cold The Colour Of Ice!

Cold the colour of ice
Winter is boring and summer is nice
Cotton on the mountains, perhaps it's ice
Winter always gives me a surprise

Be careful when you run
Cold it is but it can burn
Falling snow as light as a feather
Sunny days are much more better.

Colourless liquid have you ever thought
Springs, rivers and seas have got
Smells nothing but uses are a lot
Hard as rock when turned into ice
Try to taste the water of ice.

Ice tastes nothing, but melts in mouth,
There is more in the north and less in the south.
Taste slush and pay the price
Choose the colour of your ice.

I shiver like lightning when the winds blow
Winter came as quiet as falling snow
Snow as white as frosted glass
Covers up trees and the green grass.

Alveera Hasan (11)
The Compton School

Cold The Colour Of Ice

Cold the colour of ice
Twice, thrice I say.
If you face the ice you will pay
Many have tried and died
All that has happened is their family cried
In the North Pole
That poor lonely soul
Has faced the chill of the ice
All hopes shattered
Of him returning battered
Back home to where he belongs
All hope for him
Begins to dim.

Slowly, slowly he will freeze
Then, suddenly he blurts out in a wheeze
Cold the colour of ice.
As his time came to an end
A ray of sunshine came round a bend on an
otherwise, cold, icy day.

Joshua Logan (11)
The Compton School

Winter Is Here!

Cold, the colour of ice,
The snow settling down,
Mountains collecting more snow,
You look along the icy snowy rooftops
covered in the streets.
Children getting their mittens and scarves on
ready to play.
See everyone play in the ice,
the snow having so much fun as it's wintertime
The colour of glowing ice shows us it's time
for winter, fires, much warmth and snow.

Sophie James (11)
The Compton School

Cold The Colour Of Ice

Cold the colour of ice,
It's ever so nice.
It seems to be all I can see,
Is cold ice.

When I skate upon the ice,
I fall on the cold, ice, ice,
My ears are red,
My hands are cold,
And last of all my toes are blue.

I fall into the snow,
Look
It makes a snow fairy
It's all down our backs,
and all down my trousers.
There is some in my feet too.

Lucy Randall (11)
The Compton School

The Sun

I was walking down the street on an,
exhausting, boiling day,
I looked at the sun and I thought,
The sun using all its energy,
It was so hot that the sun calmed down
for five seconds and went to work again,
It felt like the roads and the pavements
were melting like jelly,
I looked across the road and
the people were as red as blood.
I could feel the sun on my face
like it was only on me.

Paul Alamu (11)
The Compton School

Looking Out A Morning Window

It's seven thirty or seven thirty four,
the sun's dawning this winter's morning.
Dew settles on the freshly cut grass
and people set about their daily tasks.
Some in suits carrying suitcases,
Some yacking on the mobile phones like nutcases.
An early bird chirps its lovely song
and cars zooming along
and what's that high up in the trees, not ape or an acrobat?
It's a little squirrel climbing my tree!
There's Mr Tinkler's cat stalking the street
he's a cat that no mice would want to meet.
Pretty flowers in a nice snug bed
But I'm awake and all warm thanks to my ted.
My backpack on, I'm off to school,
I'm already late, that won't do at all.

James Harvey (12)
The Compton School

Autumn And Winter

Gold the colour of autumn,
As all the russet coloured leaves
Float down from the trees.
The orange glow of the autumn sun
warming us in the early noon.
Chilly evenings with swirling autumn mists.
Thoughts of winter setting in.

Leaden the colour of a winter sky,
As full of snow as a feather pillow.
Icicles dangling from the frozen gutters,
Make me shiver and think of frozen seas.
The sound of crunchy leaves underfoot
and the wondrous sight of glittering trees.
Christmas must be just around the corner!

Luke Bonito (11)
The Compton School

A Gift From Winter

Cold the colour of ice
Ice the colour of cold
The air as icy as a frozen lake
The white-tipped mountains stand proud above the cotton-like clouds
Looking over the small village in honour
The birds fly south
To sleep in warmth
Whilst the terrorised people stare in horror
That's right
Winter's here
People beware
The time that comes around every year
The nature sits and laughs
As winter proves
That not even a thousand men
Are a match to one of winter's workers.

The air is icy,
The atmosphere bitter
The breeze sends a shiver down one's back
The frost as thick as cotton wool
The temperature so cold, it almost burns
Blue
White
Grey
The cold resembles more colours than the rainbow itself
The sheet of snow covers all creatures' eyes
So that the animals of earth don't see the pure strength and
                                      power of the winter
For the winter is an evil creature known by no man
For he has the strength of a thousand men,
The power of a thousand kings,
The speed of a thousand hawks,
The stamina of a thousand cheetahs,
But only one weakness

The cold . . .

Alexander Platts (11)
The Compton School

Cold The Colour Of Ice

Cold the colour of ice
Hot the colour of fire
Warm the colour of the sun
Lively the colour of the forest
Sadness the colour of tears
Happiness the colour of the rainbow
Anger the colour of erupting volcanoes
Sorrow the colour of the sky
Sight the colour of dawn
Hearing the colour of music
Softness the colour of clouds
Pain the colour of steel
Joy the colour of the sixties
Depression the colour of a prison cell
Peace the colour of water.

Ben Ayling (12)
The Compton School

Cold The Colour Of Ice

Cold the colour of ice,
Snow, rain and hail.
As winter comes closer,
I feel it in my fingers,
the cold, cold air.

When I go outside,
wrapped up warm in clothes,
I can still feel ice, ice, ice,
no matter what.

Winter is just around the corner,
Ice, snow, hail and rain.
Ready, ready, waiting, waiting,
for the cold, cold air.

Harriet Sweetman (11)
The Compton School

The Four Seasons

Cold the colour of ice
Bare earth beneath my feet
Cosy nests full of mice
While outside falls the sleet.

Warm the colour of yellow
Lanes to the farm so neat
With seeds all in a row
Lambs in the field go bleat.

Hot the colour of fire
Corn swaying in the fields
All the land is dryer
Dust rising from the wheels.

Mild the colour of mellow
Barns bursting with our yield
Trees lined up all a glow
While nature claims her field.

Bryony Kirkham (11)
The Compton School

Christmas

Cold the colour of ice
Snow the colour of light
Trees the colour of sugar mice
and stars the colour of life.

Toys the colour of rainbows
Sweets the colour of joy
Stockings the colour of fire
Heat the colour of jumpers.

Teddies the colour of chocolate
Greens the colour of sorrow
Sky the colour of chimney soot
and candles the colour of magic . . .

Hannah Redman (11)
The Compton School

Cold The Colour Of Ice

Cold the colour of ice

Icicles sharp as knives
In hands of children,
Playing in meadows of white.

The lake as hard as ice,
You can skate on it.

The wet dampness under your feet,
Blue all over your body.

Blizzards stalking everyone,
Towns turning into Arctic hills.

So freezing no one goes outside.

Hands shake and shiver in the air
That is too bitter to breathe.

Rosie-Lea Sparkle (11)
The Compton School

Cold

Winter is here?

Cold the colour of ice
breaks like blue and white ice
and makes us shiver
like Mum making us warm dinner.

Snowflakes float gently from the sky,
Slowly they fall passing by.
Father Christmas comes on that day,
when it starts snowing on that break.

Icicles drop and make puddles
so you need lots of cuddles.

Seema Bhagat (11)
The Compton School

The Civilian

Chosen for the challenger
Christa jumped for joy,
Not knowing that she would soon,
Follow the Devil's ploy.

She was the first civilian
To fly up to the moon,
It was a chance to die for,
Her chance would come too soon.

Selected from ten thousand
She waited in the cold,
Suspense slowly killing her,
She never would grow old.

They said there was a problem
NASA delayed the flight,
Her two children waved goodbye,
Trying to keep her in sight.

Millions saw her climb aboard
Looking ever so bold,
She strode on to the rocket,
Her death was not foretold.

The rocket, it did tremble,
The wing did burn away
The body quickly followed,
All bits did fly away.

Millions saw this happen
Millions saw her die
Christa would be remembered,
The mum who did not fly.

Sam Parlett (12)
The King Alfred School

Train Crash Ballad

I stood on the platform awaiting,
I stood there only that day.
The train pulled into the station,
To whisk me right away.

The train was running so smoothly,
When round the corner it turned
The train went off of the rails
And slowly began to burn.

The people they were all screaming
When the fuel was set alight,
Willing the doors to open up,
They got an awful fright.

The doors, they just would not open,
One man tried to be brave,
He jumped right out of the window,
But fell into his grave.

I went straight to the driver, now,
He opened the door wide,
I saw the tunnel up ahead
'Run over there!' he cried.

We ran inside the dark tunnel
Watching stunned and amazed
We watched the people crying
We watched as the engine blazed.

The fire brigade came dashing
Holding their hoses high,
The blaze was nearly out at last,
When they heard a small cry.

Three survivors, only us plus one,
The rest were killed that day
All over the news and on TV,
To Heaven they went on their way.

Chloé Hajnal-Corob (12)
The King Alfred School

Rainbow Warrior Remembered

(This poem is dedicated to the memory of Fernando Pereira - Inspired by the BBC Radio 4 programme 'The Reunion')

The French they left the harbour
And headed out to sea.
Amid the world's confusion
And loud controversy.

The Greenpeace boat went out
To an island far away.
'Rainbow Warrior' was her name,
She wasn't there to play.

The French were going to do this
Nuclear testing was their game.
Greenpeace was not going to stop them
The rainbow would not cloud their name.

The waters lapped her bow
Gaily in the light of the moon.
She was fated to sink
That night would be her doom.

The bomb went off inside the hull.
The shudder went through the ship.
People wondered what had happened
Until they realized they'd been hit.

The crew cried out into the night
How could their ship be saved?
But the lifeboats were their only choice
And they watched her sink beneath the waves.

But someone was still on board,
'He's not here,' someone cried.
He'd gone back to get his stuff,
And would not come out alive.

The photographer had gone back for his camera
But the water had got to him first.
He needed the evidence to stop the French,
That night was to be his worst.

No crying could ease the pain,
And their fists they did clench.
For the evidence pointed
Directly back at the French.

France would not say sorry
Nor deny what they had done.
The whole world couldn't believe,
That they'd killed somebody's son.

For he was a son and a young man
Adventurous and free
No one would believe
That he'd end up under the sea.

So now some must 'do',
And all of us must think
Of how they could have done this,
Made a Greenpeace boat sink.

The French thought they'd got rid of their problem,
But really they'd provided the flame
For a candle that was going to ignite,
Now Greenpeace was no longer tame.

They'd angered the world immensely
And Greenpeace was getting the money
And the publicity it needed
For the French it was no longer funny.

The big guns will play dirty
But won't always come top in the fight.
Remember, David took on Goliath
And came out, on the side of the right.

Katy Fallon (12)
The King Alfred School

The Fall Of The Mighty

The queen of all ships set sail,
On a beautiful day in April.
A near miss with the New York,
Said her voyage would be fateful.

After five hundred and nineteen miles,
An iceberg ripped open her hull.
Five compartments filled with water,
Shattering the night-time lull.

The stars lit up the sky,
And no one saw the flare.
The band just kept on playing,
And the dancers had not a care.

'Save yourself while you can!'
Cried the captain to his men.
But they kept the fire going,
Until the very end.

Down sank the ship like an angel
To the floor of the icy sea.
There she will lie in silence,
Where it's cold and dark as can be.

As the screams of the night died away,
And the bodies sank to the deep,
A silence came over the survivors.
Then all began to weep.

In the light of the early morning,
As the sun rose up from the sea,
Over the horizon came the Carpathia,
The first boat on the scene.

They said she'd never sink,
That she'd out sail them all.
But there she lies on the bottom.
The proof of her mighty fall.

The families mourned their dead.
They lie in the green Atlantic.
Now their souls are at rest,
Aboard the mighty Titanic.

Skyler Ver Bruggen (12)
The King Alfred School

The Goldfish Disaster

Poor little Stanley,
Was a small baby fish.
But today he didn't know
He would be the cat's dish.

He swam round the fish bowl,
In the usual way,
'Til his owner fed him,
And started to say . . .

'I'm going now Stanley,
I'm going away,
I'm going now Tiddles,
I'll be gone all day.'

As she slammed the door shut,
With a shuddering crash,
Tiddles the cat,
Was at the bowl in a flash.

She leaped at the shelf,
But she could not get up,
So she could not reach,
The fish she'd rip up.

She had an idea as,
She thought with a frown,
She tore at the drapes,
Which brought the bowl down.

Oh poor little Stanley,
Lay in his smashed bowl,
He flapped round in circles,
On the floor he did roll.

As the cat padded forward,
She pounced on the fish,
She gobbled him all up,
Now she'd got her wish.

When poor Mrs Puddlesworth
Walked through the door,
She saw the smashed fish bowl
And the cat on the floor.

Eddo Blundell (12)
The King Alfred School

Kew

It was the smells that hit me first,
Sweet, intense, aromatic,
It was rich, damp and humid,
The smell of the leaves.

The sight of the trees,
They were huge, green and tropical,
Some had startling colours,
The contrasts were amazing!

I felt overwhelmed,
Hot, stuffy and sticky, I looked at
The plants in the seemingly never-ending garden.
I sweated with claustrophobia.

The plants, flowers, bushes,
So colourful, so bright,
So perfectly adapted to their surroundings.

The marina world was fabulous,
All these plants that grew underwater,
Those great crabs with big pincers!

Timi Oke (11)
University College School

Happiness

Dark and humid, birds flying to capture a tasty dinner,
Chicks howling for their food, and where's Mummy?
Sun shining through the plants, they open up in joy,
Happiness for the colourful plants.

Joshua To (11)
University College School

The Man In The Glass Box

Alone in a transparent cell,
Only a few possessions,
The city around him shifts and changes,
People stand and stare,
Yet he can never reach them.

Boys arrive licking ice cream,
He reaches for his water,
Police patrol for his safety,
As entertainers come to please him,
Vandals agitate him to impress their friends.

He wraps up in his blanket,
The temperature starts to fall.
The day is nearly over,
His willpower drives him on.

Pitch-black, he stands to stretch,
The magician is a prisoner.
Trapped by his curiosity,
What are the limits of his endurance?
Who is this, incarcerated above the below?

Eden Dwek (12)
University College School

The Ice

The ice is horrible,
It's cold, very cold and painful
It's sharp and very hard
As you fall you feel the coldness on your skin
And the never-ending cold penetrates your body
Then you look up and see the icicles on the house
And you realise just how beautiful the ice really is.

Jesse Peacock (13)
University College School

Kew Gardens

In the palace of green
It was windy and wet,

Fans overhead moving the air,
Narrow pathways were winding,

Through vast glowering plants,
With a 'my territory' look,

The light was an active thing,
In the bright jade leaves,

Blinding, quite mesmerising,
The plants looked mystical, like from a fairy tale,

I was trapped in a wide ocean,
Of dark shapes and shadows,

In the desert house all was peaceful,
The plants were dead, but so riotous.

Joel Perry (12)
University College School

The Little Leaf

Summer: As light as a feather,
As green as grass,
As small as a mouse.

Autumn: As curvy as a snake,
As crusty as toast,
As gold as a ring,
As red as blood.

Winter: As dead as Hitler,
As gone as Elvis.

Spring: As light as a feather,
As green as grass,
As small as a mouse.

Samuel Barr (11)
University College School

Daddy

He was such a nice man,
Until Mummy left him,
'I love you darling, Dan,'
She said when the lights were dim.

Suddenly she went away,
It was all rather queer,
She went off up the motorway
With her handsome new dear.

Daddy was very angry,
The pub was down the lane,
He went and drunk a lot of beer,
Before hitting me again.

He brought home some beautiful girls,
Passed them money on the couch,
For him they danced and did some twirls,
But he was still a slouch.

In the morning I went up the stairs,
To bid him goodbye, as I went off,
There I was granted a life of scares,
Like cancer to a cough.

I cried and cried and cried and cried,
But all I could see was red,
I thought my mind to me had lied,
For I saw that Daddy was dead!

William Davis (13)
University College School

The Battle Of The Three To Gloucestershire

And the three soldiers rode back, deprived of their glory,
The battle had ended and they had survived,
And if that was the end, it would have ended so poorly,
But no, for they had survived
And on they rode to Gloucestershire.

The battle had been won, and they were defeated,
But in their defeat, they had survived.
They needed to go back to their homes to be greeted,
And they suffered, for they had survived.
And on they rode to Gloucestershire.

One body an inch from death, where none suffer,
But he rode on, and pushed death aside.
He went on thinking of his wife and his brother,
And thinking of the graves where his companions had died.
And on he rode to Gloucestershire.

But alas he died, and no more rode to Gloucester,
Now he was free, for he had not survived.
His body on the road, and the horse he had lost her,
And he suffered no pain, for he had not survived.

Daniel Perelberg (12)
University College School

Kew Gardens

Off the train to see the plants,
To see the geese, the gargoyles
And the fountain.

The palm house
Full of tropical plants
And dampness, mugginess and humidity.

A palm from Brazil
And the Arabica coffee plant from Kenya.
Sucking up nutrients from the rich, moisture-ridden soil.

The temperate house,
Full of plants without an extremity
And more down-to-earth plants than the palm house
But with just as much beauty as the other houses.

The Diana Spencer house,
Full of big desert plants,
This house not humid nor damp,
Just hot and dry
The perfect condition for cacti.

Jonathan Mills (11)
University College School

The Palm House

We walked inside the artificial climate,
Which felt like the home for an early primate.
The huge plants and trees towered overhead,
As if by giants watered and fed.
The small plants on the forest floor,
Looking like humidity was a bore.
The earthy musty atmosphere,
Was enough to create a sense of fear.
Up the stairs as we watched it unfold,
We were the giants of a kingdom so bold!

Ben Brooks (11)
University College School

Plants

Every plant has a weapon,
No matter how big or small,
Spikes, poisonous leaves or defiant trunks,
These plants have them all.

In the conservatory
The spiky squadron lives,
With their bulbous bodies to hold water,
They stand there like sentinels.

Now on to the Palm House,
Where trees dwarf the mighty skyscrapers,
Great weathered trunks defy the elements,
They are the strong silent ones of the jungle.

From a distance the temperate plants look peaceful,
But close up reveal thorns honed to perfection,
These subtle warriors live closer to home,
Still deadly.

David Desai (12)
University College School

Kew Gardens

K ew was fun, we never stopped,
E verything we did, we learnt something,
W alking through the various houses.

G eography everywhere,
A rt to see,
R ecognising plants we knew,
D iscovering plants we didn't.
E nglish was about feelings
N ow and then we saw something that made us
S top, and stare, and think . . .

Andrew Connick (11)
University College School

Slavery

One by one march to work,
The whip goes *crack!* and *snap!*
This work definitely has no perk,
This work is full of crap.

Barely dressed and sweating,
As they cry so much,
They treat 'em like some cretins,
This is too much cruelty as such.

Why do these people do this?
Even to their kind,
These people still exist,
Their superiors kill their mind.

So this is the end of the poem,
Please remember this,
Please go and let them,
Live in lots of bliss.

Joshua Gottlieb (13)
University College School

My Poem: The Bounty Hunter

None know her past,
None know her future,
Driven by corrupt nations,
She fights her enemies.

Frightfully beautiful,
Men drop at her feet.
Protected by foreign armour,
She blasts them all.

With one quick swipe,
She destroys Pirate research.
In attempt;
To save the Universe.

Gabriel Nowinski (13)
University College School

Nightlife

Everyone is here it seems,
People from all around.
Cars are wandering the busy streets,
And they all have their windows down.

The faint smell of expired alcohol,
With the faint sound of a train coming near.
All of this is mixed together,
To create this commercial atmosphere.

No one is silent,
Everyone is doing something,
Busy markets are over crowded,
I feel lost, as if I know nothing.

There is a queue of people with fake IDs,
With music blaring out from a door.
The smell of smoke makes me cough,
Thousands of people breaking the law.

Happy people surround me,
All probably coming home at late morning,
Thousands occupy the streets,
Until the night is dawning.

Max Bloom (13)
University College School

Tropical

The lush foliage draping down,
dense jungle atmosphere.
Fruity tropical colours
catch your every sense.
Sticky, sweaty odour
makes you faint and lightheaded,
But the wet damp space
overrules the place.

Jeremy Fitter (11)
University College School

Ballad Of A Sinner

Patience is a virtue, they said, they said,
But how can this be, if in the end we all are dead.
Waiting around does us no good,
We could run around, play games, we should.

Truth is a virtue, we're told, we're told,
'Tell the truth!' whether you're young or old,
Yet how can this be if it causes pain?
Telling the truth gives us no gain.

Pride is a sin we're scolded, we're scolded,
This is untrue; we are told and moulded,
'Believe in yourself, and in your work,'
With these words, inside us pride will lurk.

Anger is a sin they warned, they warned,
They listened, became bored and yawned,
But anger is not a sin; it's in our nature
Whether we are junior or mature.

Alex Griffiths (13)
University College School

Rollerblading

The feeling of the wind gushing against my face,
I could hear my heart beat,
Leaning down to check that I have tied my shoelaces,
Zooming down the road is a real treat,
My hair is being blown back,
Many stressful thoughts being blown to the back of my mind,
It is one of the feelings that many lives do lack,
It is a feeling I used to long to find,
Slicing through the air whilst Rollerblading,
Sometimes I start to think that the world can really sometimes be kind,
Just fading, slowly fading away,
Then I realise that I have to come back to Earth now,
And I start to come back to Earth,
A man screaming to me, 'Get off my turf!'

Jake Calvert (12)
University College School

Wilderness

I woke up brightly
And was feeling cool,
When suddenly it dawned on me
It was the first day of school.

I got out of bed
And got out the house.
My feet weren't steady
I was as quiet as a mouse.

As I approached the looming building,
And those huge iron gates,
I felt less and less confident
And started to shake.

My knees were knocking
I felt my sweaty back.
Then suddenly all I saw,
Was black, black, black.

Avi Nejad (13)
University College School

Captivating Kew

Walking through the great tall gates,
Seeing the rich brown oak trees,
It looked like a fantasy garden -
The rose bush and the pointy petals.
You prick yourself,
It sends prickles down the backs of your legs,
As the aromatic smell goes through your body,
The sound of water droplets dripping in the lake,
One after another, drip, drip, drip,
It's almost as if the cacti know
They have to protect themselves from probing hands
By making themselves untouchable
With their sharp edges.

Daniel Papier (11)
University College School

Winter

Autumn is finishing
Growing horrendously cold
Gradually getting colder
As winter draws near.

Trees are bare like statues
All hard and cold
Nothing on them at all
Leaves lost until the springtime comes
As winter is close.

Animals just settled down
Into their six month homes
Snuggling up tight
Ready to hibernate
And sleep through the cold.

Mothers and daughters
Fathers and sons
All nice and cosy
Before the first snowfall
'Wrap up warm,' all the mothers say
While children are running wild.

Sledging and snowboarding
All the different children antics
That they play enjoy
While the summer is six feet under
Buried under the leaves.

Anthony Posner
University College School

The Saga Of John Smith (Ghostbuster)

The moon was up, the sky was grey,
A lorry passed along its way,
The clock struck one,
He pulled out his gun,
And shot Josh Wade dead,
(not in heart but in the head).

Now three hundred years later,
John Smith is a waiter,
In a restaurant on the site,
(Shark Sandwich Shack, they really bite),
What John didn't know you see,
Was his psychic rating was ninety-three.

He took a shark out from the tank,
Fished fresh from the river bank,
He stabbed its heart out with a post,
He then beheld its eerie ghost,
He ran around, he screamed and shouted,
The noise of a rocket he could have outed.

He tried to hide beneath the sink,
And found a man all dressed in mink,
'Who are you?' our hero cried,
'The shock you gave me, I almost died.'
'It's over-rated you believe me,
To stay on this site for all eternity.'

'My God, you're dead!' our hero cried,
Dead Josh he leapt and John he custard pied,
But John had a blessed vacuum cleaner,
Blessed by a monk you'll find no meaner,
He sucked Josh up and now he's gone,
He threw it in the sea, this poem's done.

Peter Woolman (13)
University College School

The Winter Cold

The flakes of snow fall from the sky,
Like little drops of light,
So white against the dark city backdrop,
But it is the cold that follows that signals winter.

The children come onto the street to make the most of the snow,
Wrapped up in warm clothes,
You can hear them shout as they play,
But the cold will eventually send them in.

But still one child remains,
The cold eating at him,
He feels very little for the numbness that he has acquired,
The cold has got to him.

He remains still as a statue,
He tries to shout but the cold has shut his mouth.
His mother comes out onto the street and carries him inside.
He feels the warmth flow into his veins and chase the cold away.

By the morning the snow has turned to frost,
Cars skid on the street as they turn corners,
And the child remembers like he always will
That the cold can render you powerless.

Barnaby Spiro (13)
University College School

Kew Gardens

Bamboo sticks poking through the bars,
Huge juicy fruits hanging off exotic palms,
Earthy, leafy smell wafting in the air,
Dripping plants like stalactites in the mist.

Sound like waterfalls far off,
Towering trees like giants,
Forty feet down on ground level
Tiny grasses.
It is all living.

James Tabbush (11)
University College School

My Pets

My sheepdog is black and white,
He runs around with his feet on the ground,
He chases squirrels and rabbits for fun,
He likes to bark at anything that moves,
Which includes the postman and dustbin men.
His footpads are heard wherever he goes,
To bark at dogs and claim his domain.
He loves the heath where he can run and play,
Where there is open space to chase anything that moves.
His name is Pip.

My pets, my pets are black and white,
And like to chase and play and fight.

My small cat is black and white,
She likes to run and play and jump.
She chases mice and birds for fun,
She loves to watch anything that moves,
Which includes my feet and hands.
Her purrs are heard wherever she goes,
To fight with cats and claim her domain.
She loves the garden where she can run and play,
Where there are plenty of interesting things to watch.
Her name is Daisy.

I've got two pets who are black and white,
Who like to play and chase and fight.

David Fitter (13)
University College School

Ball

The tattered ball,
Worn down to a single flap of yellow plastic,
Slunk on the floor,
Like the runt of the litter.
Dark clouds
Hurled across the open sky,
Its passage not thought of;
To the little boy,
Opening his new toy.
The joyful cry of playing children,
Fades away into the darkening distance.
As the smell of dead rats,
Creeps its way from the garbage can.
The sky surrenders,
To the patter of rain,
Gently tapping on the torn yellow dirt.

Mike Merkenschlager (11)
University College School

Mum

She gives me life when I need it,
She helps me and gives me hope.
When I'm falling down Hell's deep dark pit,
She is there, as a shining rope.

We're bonded as long as time stands,
We're together always inside
And although fate is not in my hands,
With her my heart will always reside.

She is a star rivalling the sun,
A section of sky devoted to her.
Compare a nut when she's a plum,
She's juicier, fuller . . . much better.

A friendly bird feeding her son,
I'm so very glad that she's my mum.

Sam Briggs (12)
University College School

Rugby

A small one, a young one, a new one,
His first game, nerves, pressure, fear
So much information, so many faces shouting,
Tackle, run, pass, tackle, run, pass,
He's hit hard by a big one, an old head whose excess
weight that had ridiculed him in the classroom, now made him king,
He gets up, he's hurt, but he knows he has no choice but to continue
in the pursuit of the ball, the holy grail that must be brought
to its heavily guarded destination,
Danny has the ball, good he thinks, his majestic running can
bring only glory,
But then he's put down, the gazelle, so graceful, crushed,
The ball comes out, 'Scrum-down' calls the referee, the
almighty judge,
The players bind, forming a tank of bodies, twisting and turning
in a sphere of struggle,
It's passed down the line, a mechanical exchange from player
to player,
Then it comes to him, he sees a gap, a path to his goal,
He sprints for it, nothing else in his mind but reaching the line,
Other players look on in awe, he reaches the line,
he slams down the ball with fury, his quest was over,
The whistle is blown, the battle is over,
He who was once a cub is now a lion.

Joe Basrawy (14)
University College School

At Kew

Lush leaves sway in the breeze,
The murky water ripples as the heron dives in,
The peacock's fascinating feathers expand,
Venus flytraps snap hungrily at wandering flies,
The tropical trees tower above us.

Jacob Holder (11)
University College School

Phew It Is Hot At Kew

We finally arrived at Kew,
to find leaves dripping in morning dew.
We followed the sign to the Palm House,
where we had time to browse.

I saw elegant trees,
with multicoloured leaves.
As the strong wind blew,
some of their leaves flew.

As we walked,
along the grass we talked,
about the frail looking trees,
that could be blown away by a gentle breeze.

The Palm House was heavy with steam,
as well as being very green.
Huge plants survived in cramped pots,
although it was quite hot.

The old tattered leaves are falling,
this means autumn must be calling.
Some of the trees are beginning to look very old,
so soon it will be getting extremely cold.

Manoj Patel (12)
University College School

What Makes A Jungle!

To make a jungle four things are needed:
Plants, to make the jungle green;
Creatures, to hide in the plants;
A monster, to frighten the creatures;
And a man, to tame the monster.

Zyad Wright (12)
University College School

A Walk Through The Trees

As I wandered through the blooming trees,
Life seemed so wonderful and so worth living,
The crunching sound of shrivelled up leaves,
Gave me a tingling sensation at the knees.

I laughed at the sight of two gamboling deer,
rolling over and over waggling their ears.
I caressed the bark of a young willow tree,
Swaying in the cool, whistling breeze.

I inhaled the smell of blossoming flowers,
beautiful, tall, proud, before all.
If you think I'm making this up,
about the woods and the gamboling pups,
look around where nature is near,
what do you see, feel, smell and hear?

Michael Ostro (11)
University College School

Kew Gardens

There are palm trees
and evergreens,
Lots of plants that dance
in the sailing winds
as the others advance.

The different zones
provide many plants,
with very natural homes.

Kew Gardens is a place of nature,
where each plant has a different story
that you can read now or later.

At the end of the tour
we were tired and exhausted,
but we left Kew Gardens
having learnt much more.

Robert Germundsson (11)
University College School

The Dominating Fall

The bright red glistens in the night sky
It is coming nearer, not exactly that high
It is getting closer I can see
More and more it comes to me.

It hits that ground and pushes me away
And I see red going astray
I hit the ground harder and harder
As the red comes out faster and faster.

And then I fall
I fall, I fall, I fall
For now I am no more
No more, no more, no more.

Why has this catastrophe
Fallen upon me?
I know, I know,
It must be told

He is cold
He is old
Who is this man?
Who is the damned?

It is of course the one at hand
The one at hand
The man that's damned
That's the one at hand.

He moves so diabolically
And has left such a catastrophe
This man of course is the leader
The one who says that he's the feeder.

Of course he is a feeble man
A man he is that must be damned
This man is a stupid one
Oh why, oh why did you choose this one?

I fall, I fall, I fall.

Ramin Sabi
University College School

Kew Gardens

Trees swaying masses of trees,
Swaying in the refreshing breeze,
Kew unsurprisingly smelt like soil,
On the left I saw a lion gargoyle.

We entered the first room I think it was called palm,
It was boiling hot but I tried to stay calm,
It was so very silent not even a sound,
There were so many different shades of green around.

There were palm trees and cacti and grasses and flowers,
I could have just watched them for hours and hours.
I didn't climb up and walk all the way round,
I had too much work so I stayed on the ground.

As we moved on the flowers got brighter
As I kept snacking my lunch box got lighter,
Next place we saw was the glass house of Di,
Beautifully filled with different cacti.

The temperate house we visited first
But out of all the buildings this was the worst.
It was just like the palm house except not quite as green,
In fact there was nothing I hadn't already seen.

All too soon we were back on the train,
Twenty minutes later at Frognal again.

I'll go back to Kew Gardens, I really had fun,
I even bought a succulent, just a small one.
I'll go back to Kew Gardens, I liked every feature,
But next time I go, I won't take a teacher.

Ben Sandler-Chadwick (11)
University College School

The Cat Named Pat

There was a cat named Pat,
She was rather fat.

She could eat anything,
Except a tonne of onion rings.

When she was young,
She ate a pile of dung.

But when her mum saw what she'd eaten,
She went home and was beaten.

She cried and cried for days,
So, she and her mum went separate ways.

Finally, she was given a home,
But was chucked out for eating the phone.

So on her sixth birthday
She found that she couldn't live as a stray.

She needed an owner that would feed her well,
An owner that was caring and thought she was swell.

Unfortunately, this never happened you see,
And she died at the age of seventy three.

Ed Bailey (13)
University College School

Kew Gardens

K ew Gardens is a lovely place
E xciting, unpredictable, it's all here at Kew Gardens,
W eird plants and very pretty plants surround me all the time.

G ardens, greenhouses galore, some are hot, some are cold,
    some are neither hot nor cold,
A nd in the carnivorous plant house the Venus flytraps were busy
    trapping lots of flies,
R eally high trees in the palm house made the 'upper canopy'
    very crowded,
'D icksonia Antartica' is a lovely furry tree trunk with no leaves from
    Queensland, South Australia,
E veryone who came enjoyed themselves and had a wonderful
    time.
N umerous amounts of flies, wasps and bees were flying around,
S adly our trip to Kew Gardens has come to an end.

Adam Laikin (11)
University College School

The Culture Of Kew

Palms tower above me, the long elegant leaves
drape lazily with greens and touches of brown everywhere.
The breeze catches me as the leaves flutter silently.
Each leaf has a different shape and size,
Making them unique.

The colours refresh my mind, dazzling me with beauty
Whilst the humidity surrounds me as a bead of sweat
slides down my forehead.
The rich earthy smell of soil fills my nose
Breathing it in and out simultaneously.

Cacti everywhere with their spikes acting as daggers
Protecting the thirst quenching water.
The dry smell of sand is around me trying to take me in,
Lilies glide swiftly in the water around a patch of lilac flowers.

Jake Missing (12)
University College School

Kew Gardens

K ew Gardens is an amazing place with debonair plants
and pretty flowers.
E xciting greenhouses bustle with entertainment and colour.
W allowing waterlilies slowly waltz around the pool.

G reat fish and other underwater creatures swim in the 'Diana
Spencer Aquarium'
A utumn leaves rustle in the swift winds as they fall
to the ground
R avishing leaves block up my eardrums as I hear nothing else
D epressing sculptures and carvings parade around the gardens
E xtraordinary prices showing everywhere I go
N early all the plants in the greenhouse are exotic,
from lots of different countries and continents
S waying trees and plants look beautiful in the slight breeze.

Rohan Mulchandani (11)
University College School

An Affair

What is love? Is it only a disguise?
A frivolous mask, that angels play with?
Or a shallow façade, of blood and lies:
On a thin thread of truth, does this love live.

I lie here alone, my wife beside me,
A cold, impassive shadow by my side,
I cannot sleep, I cannot dream, nor see
But crisp, black hatred, behind whom I hide.

There lies my sword, my truth and my justice,
And may it wield the strength of great Lucifer,
And it shall be my truth and my justice,
And in the name of love, he shall suffer.

But no, how could I, I border madness:
Forever plagued by eternal sadness.

David Walsh (12)
University College School

Ode To Thy Bunnies

Oh bunnies, how your soft shiny fur shines
Oh so so softer than a baby's bum
When your ears stick up they look so divine
You may just be rabbits but you're not dumb
If you were not bunnies, then you would see
Your jumping, munching, galloping around
Plus your wonderful personality
You'd see your face when a carrot's been found
You may be arrogant, naughty and wild
But still so so sweet and cuddly and cute
Though and so better behaved than a child
Compared to a child, trouble's so minute.
You may only be just a few months old
But my love for you is wonderfully bold.

Jacob Haddad (12)
University College School

Fried Eggs

I stumble home from a brutal day of strain,
My bag is pressing upon my legs,
Only one thing in life can postpone my pain,
And that's the sizzle of those luscious fried eggs.
A snowy volcano, it turns clear to opaque,
Eruption as my fork jabs the yolk,
Two eggs like eyes staring wide awake,
And the gas cooker's flames began to smoke,
In my pan they look like giant daisies,
They bubble and quiver like a mini Etna,
Fried eggs are just another of my crazes,
They're gorgeous and flavoursome fried in butter,
My love for these calorific foods will not end,
Not until my tastes find another trend.

Josh White (12)
University College School

Shall I Compare Thee To The Moon

Shall I compare thee to the moon,
Oh you are so bright,
You are as shiny as a spoon,
If I put it in the light.

How, oh how do you shine like the starry sky?
Your beauty has touched my heart,
If you were human I'd never lie,
I hope we shall never part.

Oh moon you are the eye of Heaven,
You light up everybody's life,
I was taught what you were at age seven,
Oh you glimmer like a knife.

Oh moon how you shine,
If only you were mine.

Duncan Wilson (12)
University College School

Cheese

Oh wonderful, oh holy tasty cheese,
The flavours you exhale are so edibly rich.
I would go so far for you, and pay such high fees
I think of you as the opposite of an ugly witch
Edam is nice, but you are much better
You are strong, and flavourly mellow
You're even tastier put in a brown letter
Not black, not green, but holy bright yellow.
Once eaten, your flavour surely sticks
Before eaten, my mouth you make water.
You're there, then you're gone, after no time has ticked
Oh cheese, you're even nicer than mortar.
You are cheese, but even better and more than that,
You are eminent, all soft and squidgy flat.

Ben Lee-Rodgers (12)
University College School

It's Misunderstood

It's misunderstood the shark,
Some say it's evil and dark,
Others say its beauty is stark,
Look how gracefully it cuts an arc.

Its face displays a constant leer,
Or am I wrong is it a sneer?
I know one thing I am full of fear,
So much, I won't go near.

They swim in shallows, near the shore,
This we saw in the film called 'Jaws'.
They have fought hard to settle scores,
So now we must respect nature's laws.

To them we are the biggest threat,
I bet they wish we never met,
Many of them get caught in our net,
Maybe now's the time we pay our debt.

Manraj Lamba (11)
University College School

Kalubble-Schniff

'Tis only once, I saw a Kalubble-Schniff,
It was up the stairs in my room;
'Tis then that I smelt a wonderful whiff,
Which made my heartbeat zoom!
It sat on the floor like a cute little puppy,
And looked slightly cocking its head;
Its fur was long and smooth, yet struppy
And its nose was shiny and red.
Its feature was handsome, yet childish and playful,
And those bright, bright eyes; so full of fun!
And his little wagging tail, as soft as wool,
Seeming ready to go, to jump or to run!
So this is why I love this wondrous little muppet,
Which now while I speak, is sitting in my pocket!

Sebastian von Massow (12)
University College School

My Love Sonnet

You are as beautiful as a golden leaf
You lift my spirits like the sun at dawn
And when you go I will be only grief
And as you depart the world shall mourn.

You are as pure as a dove
And when I look into your eyes
I see the bud of love
As clear as the endless sky.

I would give my life
For a taste of your world.
I would die for you on a golden knife
As the story unfolds.

My love for you is eternal
I cannot go on with this pain infernal.

Jeremy Zucker (12)
University College School

Hull United

There's a team called Hull United
Well what can I say
They are so under-rated
Even throughout Uruguay
Though they are not in The Premiership
And they're not in the top ten
They're better than David's hairclip
And their manager's better than Glen.
They've won a few and lost a lot
And are *still* not the worst
But the one thing they've got,
And it's not being first!
It's not being last,
It's being able to last.

Saul Goldblatt (13)
University College School

Moon - A Sonnet

O moon, you are so beautiful tonight,
Within, without the starry patterned sky.
I spend hours staring at your sight.
If you were for a price, I would you buy.
Is there life beyond your deepest craters?
Your light, your face, so perfectly divine,
Not for men, for they are moonlight haters
And they do slumber when your face does shine.
Owls stay faithful, and hunt using your light.
Black, dark holes stretching down to your core,
When the sky is dark enough tonight,
Are these the many holes that men did bore?
Already and forever in your grace,
You set a match, you set a shining pace.

David Griffiths (12)
University College School

Sonnet

When I look into your eyes
And gaze upon your beautiful face,
It is like the roofless skies,
Or playing poker with an ace.
You seem to have eternal life
And have a great skill to entrance -
Without you life would be endless strife
With beauty like flowers on the plants;
As bright as the golden sun,
As quick as the dolphin leaping through waves,
My heart going like a drum -
You're the girl that my soul craves,
When you're near me, my knees turn weak
Life without you looks so bleak.

Andrew Bard (12)
University College School

My PlayStation

O PlayStation, what shall I compare you to?
You are so lovely and so favourable,
Stand you 'gainst the foot of God, I do,
You are so great, you should be an Aesop fable.

So many different games to play,
Racing, shooting or a skating game.
Play it night and play it day,
Dishonoured not, noble is your name.

You are a beautiful black box of mine,
You make the sun rise and fall each day and night,
You are no cent, you're my precious goldmine,
You should be the Great North Star cos you are so bright.

O, they've been happy times, no knocks or shocks,
But you're not as good as that green Xbox.

Arthur Coates (12)
University College School

A Sonnet To My Skateboard

Oh my darling on wheels,
All made out of wood
You remind me of meals,
That were just too good.
I use you each day,
Each hour is blessed,
But when I put you away,
You would never have guessed,
I cry, I cry, as hard as I can,
When I think of the things that are going to happen,
When I think about the ban,
That bad Ken has run,
It's terrible,
But bad Ken says it's honourable.

Nick Gourlay (12)
University College School

Ode To My Pencil Case

Oh old faithful, how simple an idea
Is based on such a complex but divine
Concept, it plagues my brain and to fear
It is so unbearable and that it's mine
Just makes it harder for I think it's all
The worse because my innocent conscience
Makes me want to succumb to it and maul it.
All these thoughts, they are such nonsense.
Its colouring is distinctly red.
Its capacity is one ruler, one pen.
I did not want to buy it, I was misled
But now I have it and I'm one of the men.
It worked hard for me and I will be
Sorry to see it go because it's me.

Ben White (12)
University College School

My Monkey

I love my monkey
I know he likes to dance
He is very funky
He can also water plants!

I think he's the best,
He's absolutely great,
He is better than the rest,
He's my best mate!

He suddenly ate a bat,
Then he lost a toe,
He then got bitten by a cat,
Who then became his foe!

My monkey loves me,
And I love he.

James Bullock (12)
University College School

Ode To A Sunday Morning Lie-In

Oh Sunday morning lie-in you are sublime,
I adore thee immensely my sweet lovely darling,
I lie in my snug sheets unaware of time,
Oblivious to my agitated parents' snarling.
What would I do without thee, I would falter and die,
I need your warm embrace, your beautiful cover.
All I need is you, and a steak and kidney pie,
And soon all I shall hear is the fury of my mother.
Soon I shall have to get up and put on shoes
And trousers, pants, and a ghastly tartan shirt.
Oh getting up gives me such terrible blues,
And the shirt makes me look like my piano teacher Bert.
If I get up the cold will give me flu,
Oh Sunday morning lie-in I love you.

Archie Johnston-Stewart (12)
University College School

Kew!

Kew, Kew, why do we bother?
Not for the drizzle,
but for the brilliant sights -
tree webs, cacti
the carp
in their swimming pools.

Kew, Kew, why do we go?
For the jungle,
the temperature,
in the soaring Palm House.

Kew, Kew, what do we do?
We dehydrate,
David Blaine style,
and we look at green,
admiring leaves.

Sebastian Silverman (11)
University College School

Kew

Huge plants glaring at me,
Startling colours flashing,
Bamboo poking at me,
Luscious fruits off exotic trees.

Trees like poles holding up the building,
Towering trees making me feel tiny.
Budding flowers popping up all colours.
Huge pointed leaves on the stick-like palms,
Trees with pine cone textures.

The smell of fresh soil spluttered across the ground,
Earthy, leafy smell.

Max Rosenthal McGrath (11)
University College School

Rainforest

The amazing tropical rainforest
covered in lush green,
so many brilliant trees,
a wonder to be seen.

So hot and humid,
the air is very dense.
It is all so lurid
It makes you feel tense.

The trees are all different:
some hold glorious fruits,
some provide medicine,
some are just roots.

Tom Bradshaw (11)
University College School

Kew Gardens

The vibrant colours enter my brain,
Like a giant multicoloured stain,
The red and white oriental fish play tag,
As ten gawping boys look in vain,
The pure white geese paddling along,
As you watch them they're incredibly tame.

The Palm House is made of clear glass,
The plants can see the people pass,
Kew Gardens is absolute class,
So much to see sky scraping trees,
And a cactus so high it could die.
Palm trees swishing in the breeze,
And ten plump bumblebees.
An earthy smell came out of its shell,
As I entered the hot humid hell.

Bushes blushing bright as cherries,
Reminds me of those Christmas berries,
I hope the time will never go,
As the Kew glass buildings glow,
And everybody's feelings show,
We flow out of the enormous gates,
And make our way to the train,
We jump on our train with our faces looking plain,
We stepped off the train and it looked like it was
                                        going to rain,
It was a real shame.

Leif Wild (11)
University College School

The Portal

A lake of fate awaits,
upon it a rowing boat is moored.
There is only a captain,
all his crew, lost.
They live in the abominable depths of the lake,
Unknown to be dead or alive.
The captain's face wretched and scarred
by the madness that lies over him,
stays dull all the time.

But when the moonlight shines upon him,
his bony body fills with something -
not love, not happiness, not depression -
it fills with fear.
His mind, his spirit-tormented mind,
cradles after the same figure walking towards him,
another passenger,
or victim.

Gone,
gone again.
When the moonlight clouds over,
nothing is to be felt,
nothing is to be seen,
only troubles,
that glide over the water's gleam.
What can it be?
Nobody knows.
Maybe his crew is walking away,
walking somewhere . . .
A duty of darkness,
entering the gates of Hell.

They torture him,
again and again.
The captain's scream of terror
fuels them, feeds them.
But why?
- because the captain is covered by something.

The captain is covered with something.
He is caged in a life,
a life of foul deeds,
he is immortal,
cannot get out.
He does not know what awaits him,
the horrors of his fate.

He wishes that one day
an angel will unlock his cage of fate
and guide him through the portal
of peace, of life.

Thomas Bruce-Clayton (12)
University College School

Kew Gardens

The rusted gates, wide open,
bringing the aroma to passers by.
The scent of flowers speaks their beauty,
to tourists from all around the world.
It is a remedy for a depressed photographer:
a symmetrical continuous view.
Plants of all categories,
accumulate from every crevice of Earth.
The gigantic palm trees stand, waving like umbrellas.
A perfect sight as the light glitters on the leaves.
The pink lotuses proud of their dresses,
float around the lilies in a fashion show.
Colonies of flies vote their plant president
for its nectar dessert.
Prickles of cacti frighten their predators,
Their arid nature full of hate.
These plants of all sizes, the luxurious creations of the Almighty,
here in urban Richmond.
Where everybody comes to adore
These passive, mute beings in
The botanical garden of Kew.

Suraj Kadiwar (11)
University College School

Cinderella Reloaded

As you know, Cinderella got her man,
But do you know what happened next?
An unexpected visitor turned up
That left the bride most vexed.

The wedding day soon came around,
All were dressed in style.
The congregation gasped in awe
As Cinderella walked down the aisle.

Prince Charming stood there waiting for her,
Their eyes met and filled with love,
The union of a special couple,
Blessed from above.

The vicar stood before them,
As they prepared to take their vows.
The door opened behind them
As someone else joined in the crowd.

The ceremony went quite smoothly,
The congregation swelled in song,
But then the moment happened
When everything went wrong.

'Does anyone have a reason
Why this marriage should not be blessed?'
A woman at the back stood up
And shouted loudly 'Yes!'

The bride and groom both turned around
And looked to the back in fright,
They were shocked to see who was standing there -
Could this really be Snow White?

'Prince Charming promised to marry me!'
She cried as she sank to the floor,
She lifted her head to gaze at them
And then gave off a roar.

This wasn't the man she thought he was,
Who'd left her in the lurch.
She was mortified to realise
She had come to the wrong church.

Snow White ran out of one door,
Cinderella ran out of the other,
Which left poor Charming standing there,
All flushed under the collar.

Cinderella caught up with Snowy
And demanded an explanation.
'I seem to have made a mistake' she cried,
'Upon further examination.'

Cinderella smiled in great relief,
And rushed to find her man.
They went inside together again
And the wedding went on as planned.

Edward Alexson (12)
University College School

Africa

Ravaging birds, racing cheetahs
Laughing Hyenas.
A crackle of a gun
And a lion's howl.

We travelled the Namib Desert
Rocky plains and barren land.
We stopped to rest by a baobab tree
Where birds sang their sweet song.

Then came the night
Where fire flickered
Throughout the desert.
Stories we told whilst roasting
marshmallows.

The howling, the roaring, the singing
Played their part as we slept.
The animals awoke to start their day.

Joshua Lever (11)
University College School

A Trip To Kew Gardens

The tulips, cactus and the bamboo
They all come from Kew Gardens
You can't find these plants at London Zoo
My breath shortens and hardens.

Your first sight as you come through the gate
Is the murky pond water
It's the kind of place where frogs might mate
They're practically slaughtered.

Next was Marrianne North's gallery
Her paintings were a big shame
Her sheep look like my friend Valerie
Her landscape pictures are lame.

So I quickly ran to the desert house
My group, they shared my feeling
There were plants with names I can't pronounce
And one that started peeling.

Next was the temperate house
It was hot, we wanted out
We sweated like pigs, no not a mouse
My friends agreed there's no doubt.

The site on its own has an image
An image of plants and trees
You get there by crossing the dream bridge
Or paying 50p.

I've told about my trip to Kew
Your view puts you in a trance
I have told you about London Zoo
And how the sunflowers dance.

So I've only got one thing to say
See Ya Kew! Another day.

Jonathan Cartier (11)
University College School

Island

A hot wind, boiling and intense.
Two things - humid and tense.
The air scarred and burnt the salt on my face,
As I saw the island for the first time.

Palm trees swept brushes over the sand,
The wind whistled as my heart beat in my hand.
Death lingered high above my head,
My feet could not move, seemed made of lead,
As I saw the island for the first time.

As I walked under a canopy of green,
Bamboo stood tall and lean,
One stalk stronger than a man's bone
Can lift a weight bigger than its own,
As I saw the island for the first time.

Shadows started to block the rays of light,
A black cape came over and soon it was night.
Eyes stared at me from a distance
And now and then cried out to show their existence,
As I saw the island for the first time.

Hunger and fear crept into my head,
Terror as I imagined the picture of me dead.
Now reality settled comfortably over me,
I was a poor boy on an island lost out at sea,
As I saw the island for the first time.

I desperately fumbled for fruit in the tree,
One came into grasp - but poisonous as fruit can be.
My stomach turned, my insides wrenched through my jaw.
I twisted and turned, writhing on the floor,
As I saw the island for the first time.

Blurred monsters and shapes danced round my legs,
I looked at my vomit: like a mixture of eggs.
I felt so small, a useless wimp,
Then everything blackened as my body fell limp,
And I saw the island for the last time.

Louis Butler (12)
University College School

Kew

Strange green sunshades,
In obscure shapes,
Conceal creatures, jumping from tree to tree.
But you never know,
You never see,
Because they're hidden in the canopy.

Underneath the giant green leaves,
In the shadow of a tree,
There's a tempting smell,
Some sticky leaves,
A wet, spiky death for an unknown insect.

A salivary mouth
That was full of ants,
Munched the deadly plant,
Until a spike sank into his mouth.
Shrieking wildly,
The anteater thundered through the forest,
Tearing bushes apart,
As a few half dead ants
Staggered from its mouth.

Alfie Lake (11)
University College School

Morning

The sun's rays pierce the cold morning air,
and a blood-red sky falls upon the clouds
The roads lie still as people stir in their beds,
Like a desolate city, so peaceful.

The roads become full of purposeful workers,
Their car horns like an orchestra,
Each person playing on their own accord,
No more this peaceful city but a commercial metropolis
Until tomorrow morning.

David Naftalin (14)
University College School

The Person Inside

I sit here and cry
Watching people walk by
They look back at me
But all I can see
Is the person inside
The side that they want to hide.

I lie down and sleep
The people think I'm a heap
They judge me unfairly
But I think quite contrary
And all that I know
Just goes to show
That it's the person inside
The side that they want to hide.

Elliott Smith (11)
University College School

Simone, The Winter Hater

Winter is a peaceful time
A time for love and caring
It also is a time for rhyme
And poems that are daring;
While snowflakes fall upon the ground
And people sit at home
There is nothing outside the sound
Of a woman called Simone.
'I care not for this winter thing'
So muffled is her voice
'And why do stupid people sing
Dumb carols and rejoice?'
The people just ignore Simone
She sits in the snow and groans alone.

Theodore Weiss (13)
University College School

The Piranha

At the bottom of the river there waiting,
Waiting to sniff your blood and attach without you noticing.
They are vigorous eaters, eating whatever they can.
They can bite through your flesh and cause mayhem around the
world.
You will never notice it until blood and skin rises to the surface of
the water.

Piranhas come in all shapes and sizes,
They may look harmless but are nasty creatures.
Their teeth are deadly and needle-shaped
Used for cutting and tearing off chunks of flesh from their prey.
Their tails are arrow shaped which makes them very fast and good
at turning
So the next time you swim in a river, just beware of what lurks
below the surface.

Alastair Danzig (11)
University College School

Chess

I see him every day sitting on my table,
Leader of his kingdom,
Advisors beside him,
An army in front,
The field is made of black and white mountains,
He waits patiently for their move,
Strategically planning his pieces,
His knight set in position,
His rooks on either side,
His wife bravely goes into battle,
All is at stake,
If she is captured, maybe all is lost . . .

But remember it's only a game.

Adam Allybokus (11)
University College School

The Palm House

That's the sound of water, when it's dripping on the floor,
In the Palm House.
You may think it's a bore,
But it's so humid and hot, you just wanna get a claw
And rip it all down and get out
Into the fresh air and stare at the teacher's evil glare, at
Oli when he's spiking his hair,
With the water from the palm house.

When you climb to the top and survey the scene,
When you see where you're going,
And look where you've been,
The world all around you is full and dense
And the air is so moist
And the view is so green.
The vastness of jungle
Surrounds you with steam,
Your spirit has travelled
To a rainforest dream . . .

So now we descend to the depths below ground,
To drop many feet, to plunge down and round,
The spiral staircase,
Which takes you right under.
You're now on a seabed
And wide-eyed with wonder . . .
The marine life which dazzles,
The colours spellbind -
The Palm House has caught you
And invaded your mind.

Jake Miller (11)
University College School

Desert Island

Why does this sea slap the shore?
Although it's a beauty,
I wish for no more!
All I want
Is to be free,
Enough of this island,
Enough of this sea!
I try to stay calm,
Again and again,
Though I cannot feel anything
Except for the pain.

I still hope that I
May stay alive,
For if I find food,
I am bound to survive.
Though no food yet -
My stomach is churning,
I just can't think straight,
My mind's tossing and turning.
Still I have faith
That soon I'll be freed
Far from this death-hole,
Far from the sea.

Leo Seigal (12)
University College School

New York

The smell of hot dogs,
The cigarette burns,
The all-night diners,
The city lights shine like stars,
The Broadway shoes,
The streets are yellow,
Filled with taxis,
The big burgers,
The greasy kitchen,
The delis,
The shopping malls,
Huge range of clothes,
The stench of perfume flying up my nose,
Yes it's New York City.

Akhil Kumar (11)
University College School

The Leaf

Its short little life
over in a few months -
the first moment it's green,
the next it's red.
All its friends
still left on the tree.
All alone
It blows away.
In the end
it falls to the ground,
so red
it's bleeding.

Tai-Li Lee (11)
University College School

Christmas

I wait day by day for it to come,
For the presents to come filling in, an innumerable sum.
I can't sleep at night and can't work at day,
And when I go home, I can't help myself but to play.
Even though I know that Father Christmas is fake,
I just wish he was there so my presents did not come late.
I often have thought of what I am going to get,
But when I open the wrapper, it is not what I expect.
I love helping my mum when putting up the Christmas tree,
And getting all the equipment out to make the holly.
I go upstairs and show the Christmas tree to my dad,
And the only comment he can say is 'Not bad!'
This is because he doesn't enjoy it as much,
Because he thinks the best part is the Christmas lunch!
He doesn't like the idea of hanging things on the walls,
And especially when he has to pick up the tree when it falls.
I love Christmas mainly because of the presents,
And going to Church, to help the independence.
I invite friends round to my house to stay,
And when I wake up the next morning, I realise that it was just
                                                        another day.

Payum Partovi (11)
University College School

The Witches (In The Style Of Shakespeare)

In the cauldron goes these things
Wasps and bees and all their stings
Lions teeth, a tiger's roar,
In the cauldron throw a boar.
Intestines of a dying rat
Ears of bunny, eyes of bat.
Dinosaur's spikes, a dragon's lurk;
It has to be evil for it to work.
Double, double, toil and trouble,
Fire burn and cauldron bubble.
Old man's toes and knobbled knees,
Ice so cold, some of this will freeze.
Worms and bugs and all strange creatures,
All that come in unique features.
The skeleton of an alligator,
Will fry it, poach it and boil it later.
Double, double, toil and trouble
Fire burn and cauldron bubble.
Rooks that have lived for years and years,
The smallest elephants, the biggest deer.
Double, double, toil and trouble
Fire burn and cauldron bubble.
This potion may show you of some death
So look out and watch this, Macbeth.

Jamie Fireman (11)
University College School

Surviving Kew

Psychedelic flowers bloom up in front of me,
A wonderwall flaming with vibrant colours,
Sweet roses twinkle in the sunlight,
Lavish smells surround me - luring me into their charms.
The fountain laughs, sprays water like a baby elephant,
Mesmerising petals, and the freshness in the air.

But then the greenhouse
And the sun dies,
Hot and humid,
Dark and sweating,
Ivy sprawls everywhere -
An imperial army invading
Another country,
Berserk exotic plants. Stunned. Electrocuted.
Colossal overwhelming trees tower over me,
Trapping, terrifying, tormenting.
Cacti with spikes as sharp as Spartan spears
Pierce deep,
Gargoyles gaze in gruesome fascination.

I storm the exit,
Out in the sun and air at last.
But now, an ambush.
Evil geese rampaging ravenous
For a cheese sandwich.
I run for my life, the bus in my sights.
Survived the school trip for another year!

Chris Fox (11)
University College School

Kewdrops and Sunshine

Kew Gardens with your lush lilies,
each one contains a memory.
Never-ending beauty,
deserted plains and great, tall trees.
Rich, damp views with every blink,
or dry, arid overwhelming heat.
Perhaps that's not the best of it -
smelling rich leaves with every breath.

Note the cacti -
never leave the will to stay alive.
Dangerous, delicate and rare
plants all live in Kew Gardens.

Aromas everywhere, it's claustrophobic
to smell humidity in the air, disorienting,
Rich textures fill every cranny,
give your brain too much.
Heavy feelings loll around,
in the houses of Kew Gardens.
Never leave this Earth until
you have visited this place.

Harley Sugarman (11)
University College School

Ode To Kew, Our Trip In Several Parts

I

O smashed Silverlink Trains,
Does your paint come off when it rains?

II

O Ivy, you are green,
You are the greenest thing
I've ever seen.

III

O naming signs, memorials
Doomed to sit in the ground
Or hang off trees,
You who inform us of names,
We salute you.

IV

O carp! You are orange
With black dots. I wonder if
Fish get spots?

V

O great wad of dirt!
When you get stamped on,
Does it hurt?

VI

O spiky tree up in the sky,
Do you ever want to fly?

VII

Roses, roses in the ground,
So perfect and so round!
You do not know what lies ahead
When summer's gone
And the sun is dead.

VIII

O weeping willow,
Why do you weep so?
Is it time, is it decay?
Is it knowledge?
You'll never say.

IX

Cactus, cactus in the sand,
Why do you prick my hand?
It would be nicer, don't you see,
Instead, just to welcome me.

X

Silver van, at you I cannot scoff,
Although someone's smashed
Your wing-mirror off.

Nat Bury (12)
University College School

Winter Days

Winter's starting
It's grey, dark and cold
Everyone's parting
Because they're ill and old.

She's gone and dead
And there's no one instead
He's left alone
To fend on his own.

The end of a lifetime
Signals the end of the day
The end of the night-time
Says morning's on the way.

Lucas Giles (11)
University College School

San Francisco

My native country
My favourite city
The Golden Gate
Playing with my cousin Nate
The big green parks
The sandy beaches
The bay and the ocean
With such a smooth motion
Not a single commotion
All the nice smells
The ding-dong of the ferry bells
How I would love to live there
With the wind whooshing my hair
It's just so pretty
My native country
My favourite city.

Henry Fuz-Keeve (11)
University College School

The World

People dying
Children lying
People helpless
Children left hopeless
Rape, murder
Let's not take it any further
Children left
People committing theft
People swearing
Children think that they're daring
Suddenly a person cried
And before you know it someone has just died.

Eliot Tang (12)
University College School

X-Men

Xavier, Jean and Cyclops,
Wolverine and Storm.
You've marched around in costumes,
Since the day you were born.

You're the X-Men of this world,
You save us every day.
The enemies of yours are hurled,
Through the mud and hay.

You've saved my life on countless times,
I thank you with all my heart.
Especially the redhead girl,
And the blue one that's so smart.

You're the X-Men of this world,
You save us every day.
The enemies of yours are hurled,
Through the mud and hay.

Jubilee and Marrow,
You're the youngest of them.
And it's thanks to both of you,
That there is such mayhem.

You're the X-Men of this world,
You save us every day.
The enemies of yours are hurled,
Through the mud and hay.

So goodbye my dear X-Men,
I bid you all farewell.
I'd like to take this time to say,
That you're all really swell.

The X-Men.

Connor Davis (13)
University College School

In The Park

As I walk through the gates, a sudden overwhelming noise of
toddlers and footballers, playing as the wind rushes through my hair.

We clench hands, and the warmth of our fingertips runs through into
our bodies and bloodstream and the shoes that we wear.

As I walk, I can feel the crunch of the autumn leaves, under my feet
as they scatter around me.

And when I breathe out, I can see my white breath for a few seconds
as we approach the willow tree.

I swing up on one branch, and one more, and another.

I keep swinging as my hands keep on just getting rougher.

When I look out over the grass, frost lies quietly on the brim

And as I stamp over the grass a sensational feeling flies up through
me, limb by limb.

We approach the exit and we rejoice our hands as warmth spread
through me again.

Like a squirrel with food for its family heading back to the den.

Patrick Mayer (12)
University College School

Holocaust

Imagine waiting in fear,
Waiting for the unknown,
Lying in a bunk crammed with people,
Each one as starving as the next.

A man sits on the floor,
Telling the Passover story,
Of the liberation of the Jews from Egypt a thousand years ago.

Imagine waking up to the smell of burnt bodies wafting through
the air,
Bodies of your friends, people you once knew,
Your neighbours, wives, brothers, sisters.

Imagine working, each day, in the mud without food,
Imagine that you have forgotten the miraculous taste of freedom,
Imagine that you have lost all hope and faith.

Imagine not having a name,
But instead, a number,
Imagine living in the constant shadow of death.

Just imagine.

Michael Kosky (12)
University College School

Tarantula Thoughts

I am a tarantula with eight hairy legs,
I hatched from one of a thousand eggs.
I only have six brain cells and a very tiny brain,
My web is full of tiny bits of little flies, I've slain.

I live inside the science lab, under the science teacher's care,
He gives me a bath three times a week, and even combs my hair.
I look outside my box at all the children gaping,
'Teacher! Teacher!' they all cry, 'the spider he's escaping!'

'Now you stay in your box young man,' I've often been told.
Ever since I was found, put on the market and sold.
But being the science lab spider, is really very cool,
because there are not too many spiders,
    who go to a private school!

Ed Klinger (11)
University College School

Too Many Tears

All people see what's going on in the Middle East,
Where there's so much tension you can hardly breathe,
It's sad when people cry and die for their races,
And when on television you see the starved kids' little faces,
Every day we pray for God to do his work,
And get these kids out off the filthy dirt,
Together let's pick ourselves up and rise above and out of the mist,
And show the kids that there's an end to all this,
This means every single one of us were all affected,
We need to stop worrying about being so protected,
So let's all fight to get ourselves respected,
Men and women please look after your kids,
So when you come home you will get a kiss,
Don't worry when this is over the look in their eyes,
Relieved, bright warm and happy no more goodbyes.

Jacob Butchoff (12)
University College School

The Tramp

Me, the tramp, walking along the road.
Dragging both dog and sleeping bag by my side.
Labrador, big no more, a skinny, scruffy, scrawny thing standing by
my side.
More dependant, more trusting than a blind man on his fingers.
People look in disgust at a hairy ogre walking down Oxford Street,
that's me.
I get laughed at by teenagers in flashy clothes.
Ninety pence, one pound fifty a day, enough to live on.

Evening, a time for rest, no, still walking.
Bus stops, a shop front, what a place to sleep.
Three drunks swagger past, laughing, a dream, a wonderful dream.
Don't even notice as I walk past, that's a novelty.
No dirty looks, no catcalls, nothing except the sound of their laughter
and swearing.
Woolworths, a worthy place to spend another night alone.
I snuggle up in my sleeping bag, my house, my only refuge.

Me, the tramp.

Ben Skerritt (13)
University College School

Music

When music enters your ears,
You feel different things and lose all your fears.
Many people like different styles,
Hip hop, rock, classical, the list goes on for miles.

Music can make you feel happy or sad,
Excited, nervous, emotional or mad.
You can listen to music at home or in clubs,
In the car, at parties or even in pubs.

Music is vital, it helps our world go round
Especially here, we love the London sound.
That is why I think music is so unique,
And that is why I listen to it every day of the week.

Roie Spitzer (13)
University College School

Neighbours

In your time here and now,
You only hear the old row,
But neighbours are otherwise not too bad,
Unless they are absolutely mad!

But back in my time (1154),
A disagreement between neighbours would shake the floor.
Battlements, arrows, trebuchets and more,
Hundreds of bodies on the floor!

Hiding behind battlements while your energy fades,
While within the keep the bustle of trade.
Walls are collapsing, fires spread,
The man on your left falls off the walls, dead.

So just remember when you complain,
About a noisy neighbour shouting again and again,
What it was like when sieges were fought,
And you probably won't give it another thought!

David Barton (12)
University College School

My Family

He's mean and strict like my mother,
He's smart and cautious, he's my brother.

My older sister Abigail,
Always leaves a messy trail.

My sister Danielle is very loud,
She is the loudest in her crowd.

My father went to UCS.
At being naughty he was best.

My mum is always on the phone,
Whether out and about or at home.

As for me I am the sweetest and best,
And definitely better than all the rest.

Michael Genis (12)
University College School

The Last Ever Soul

The lucid horizon composed by nature,
Is all that remains.
Oceans are now still, no tempests to fashion chaos.
The land is frozen,
But the last ever soul remains warm.
It is the essence of all existence,
That ever did and did not.

The silence is piercing like a subtle blade.
Time is nonsense here,
But what was now
And what is then?

The soul thinks to itself,
As it had done eternally.
Would anything change if existence ceased?
Soon no one will know.

Svilen Mirtchev (13)
University College School

Why?

Why do I wake up at seven?
Why not half-past eleven?

Why do I get dressed?
Why can't I show my best?

Why do I go to school?
Why because it's hardly cool?

Why do I do my work?
Why not be a twerp?

Why do I have to go to bed?
Why can't I go paint the town red?

Why not?

Max Sopel (14)
University College School

As The Bear Walks Down The Road

As the bear walks down the road,
People are scared and the noise is on overload.
It tramps along,
With its distinctive pong.
On and on and on.

As the bear walks down the street,
It will kill people that it is bound to meet.
With its sharp claw,
That tore my dog's paw
Into piece after piece.

As the bear walks down the lane,
As people are hurt they are in pain.
A punch is no match,
To the bear's deadly scratch.
Which tears and tears and tears.

As the bear walks down the avenue,
People try to get it away by saying 'Shoo.'
But it carries on killing,
An episode that's thrilling.
That finishes with the shot of a gun.

Max Coventry (11)
University College School

Hunting Mully The Great Kangaroo

The sun beat down,
I had a frown,
I hadn't found her yet.
She certainly wasn't a pet,
Seven-foot high,
No, I don't lie,
She could rip anything apart,
And she was extremely smart,
So I took my knife, and I took my gun,
Unfortunately they weighed a ton.
I hid beneath a holly bush,
And waited on my itchy tush.

The Australian outback is always rife,
With scorpions and snakes and strife,
But this monster was new to me,
I cried, 'That ain't no wallaby!'
But that was ten years ago,
Now she's my Moby Dick, you know.
And now I'm back to find her,
But who will commit murder?

Josh Jackman (13)
University College School

Teachers

Some are fun, some are boring,
Some won't realise if you're snoring.

Some are young, some are old,
Some have hair, some are bald.

Some are thin, some are fat,
Some won't realise if they've squashed a cat.

Some are short, some are tall,
Some know just as much as the inside of a ping-pong ball.

To them we are toys,
Us poor little boys.

In maths we learn geometry and symmetry that
puts us to sleep,
Then our maths teacher comes round and
says 'Wake up you creeps.'

They always try to put you in your place,
And sometimes you wish you could send them
to outer space.

They are inhumane with their threats and detentions,
Just if we don't listen and pay attention.

They are always biased to the kids that always work,
I really do think that some of them are jerks.

They try to teach us rugby but they don't know
themselves,
Even the teachers who are no bigger than elves.

I don't really like teachers, I don't know about you,
I really think that they should be locked away in
the zoo.

Zak Beller (12)
University College School

All Alone In The Playground

All alone in the playground,
I really don't like that.
All alone in the playground,
I feel like a little rat.
All alone in the playground,
Feeling sad as could be.
All alone in the playground,
No one will play with me.
All alone in the playground,
The others are playing games.
All alone in the playground,
They jeer and call me names.
All alone in the playground,
I wish the break would end.
All alone in the playground,
I wish I'd find a friend.
All alone in the playground,
Waiting for the whistle to blow,
All alone in the playground,
Time passes ever so slow.
All alone in the playground,
How I wish that I could play.
All alone in the playground,
It's never a happy day.
All alone in the playground,
There's another boy like me.
All alone in the playground,
Maybe friends we shall be.

Loni Levy (12)
University College School

A Warrior's Troubles To A Perfect World

The black ash,
The burnt timber,
The smell of slowly decaying corpses,
Rotting skin,
The termites come out to play,
A blast of light,
A shrill scream.
The whistle of a bomb,
Slowly falling to its doom
And many others,
The laughter of peril,
As German planes fly overhead,
Missiles launch ploughing through the smoky air,
It hits like an arrow aiming for the heart.

A bullet hurries
A journey ended.
A piercing cry,
Another journey up to Heaven.
A smothering coat of black fog,
A shout of terror,
'Gas!'
Lungs ruptured,
Pleading for death,
It comes swift on its black chariot,
A wicked grin on its gleeful face,
As it repays his anger on you,
Then suddenly it's gone,
You float up on your happy road to Heaven.

Elliot Lowe (11)
University College School

My Special Place

For the second time
I went to Kew
I wasn't looking forward to it,
I didn't know what to do.
Should I injure myself
Or should I fake a fall?
Because last time was such a disaster.
The only fun part last time was rolling down a hill.
I came along anyway
Trying to forget the last one
And I was really surprised when I got home,
Because it was actually really fun.
I was in Mrs Anthony's group
And I was given the camera,
Only because in the JB
I was the camera master.
We first went to the hot palm tree house
It is boiling in there I must warn
And it is absolutely soaking as well.
You'd think there had been a storm.
We went to the Diana Reed's house
The Temperate and those Chinese towers
Not to mention we also saw
quite a few hundred flowers.
Through the other houses we went
Across the lakes and streams
The rushing water and flowers
Made you feel you were in a field of dreams
In my special private place
Which I embrace.

Dan Kagan (11)
University College School

Doing A Maths Test

I sit down at my desk
And start at question seven,
Wait a minute what does all this mean
Pi add five take away eleven?
This doesn't mean a thing . . .
I think I better start it all again.

This time I will do better,
I'll use my lucky pen,
I'll do this question in time,
I'm doing well but then . . .
The hypotenuse?
I think I better start it all again.

Now I'll really crack it!
I'll do better than my brother Ben!
My parents will be proud of me,
And I'll be in the league of gentlemen,
Oh I'm getting really stuck,
I think that I should start it all again.

I'm the only one who's not writing,
And the test is coming to an end,
The clock has just stopped,
I feel as stupid as a chicken or a hen,
He's taking in my paper,
(Sir, please can I start it all again?)

Matty Bradley (13)
University College School

The World

The world today is a terrible place,
There is crime and corruption in the human race,
People carry guns and knives,
Always threatening other people's lives.

There is pollution in every ocean and sea,
But this problem has no door or key,
There is rubbish lurking wherever you look,
There is fast food taking the place of a cook.

There is technology for everything you do,
Expensive packaging wasted on you,
You don't do anything for yourself any more,
Just go to a computer to sweep up the floor.

The kids of today just spend their money in shops,
You don't see kids in the pool doing bellyflops,
You see kids with their mobiles and mini TVs
You never hear the kids saying thank you or please.

Forget technology and this robot life,
See real people in need and strife
Understand children need to play,
In a natural world where they can have their own say.

Then you will see the world in a better way
When the sun comes up every day,
You can then hope this planet will see the light,
And rid the world of this terrible blight.

Adam Cartier (12)
University College School

The Tramp

Every day sitting in the loneliness
Sitting in the shadows of the sun
All he did was watch people pass by
As he would sit there begging.

He would get the odd coin here and there
But would only spend it on drink to drown his sorrows
His clothes would smell and would be dirty
As he would never wash.

He would walk from town to town
What he needed was to do something
But he couldn't afford anything decent
He didn't have talent so there was nothing for him.

He would try to sleep at night
In a tube station if he was lucky
But all he could think about was his damp life
He would think that is life always going to be this hard.

As time grew on the tramp became old
And was too tired and frail to be homeless
He died at an unfortunate age
With no one ever knowing who he was.

He could have had a good life
But he wasn't given that chance
So nothing ever happened
He was just a lonely man who left this world unnoticed
Without saying goodbye to anyone.

Daniel Perkins (13)
University College School

Memories From Dunkirk

Staring,
Staring out into the once cabbage-green sea
At the devastating scenes,
Hellish fights for survival.
A few of us perch in our makeshift bomb shelter
Anxiously waiting for evacuation boats.

The first glimmer of hope is cruelly wiped out,
Just as we were getting up and out of the shelter,
The boat hits a mine.

We endure a few more hours,
Telling stories about the good times and wonderful England,
But the sharp, bitter cold gets the better of a few.
More hours of desperately hoping pass.
Hoping the circling fleet above won't spot us.
Hoping for a boat to arrive.

Despite the bite of ice on my hands
I wave frantically on the arrival of a boat,
As my whole outlook turns from black to white in a second.
I hurry up the sand and clamber onto the boat
And sleep in the knowledge that my whole world was fine.

I wake on a damp boat filled with the stench of rotting wood and fish,
But nothing so trivial can ever matter to me again.
I'm back in the glorious English sea,
The sea between my heavenly home
And the hellish Dunkirk shore.

Ryan Corcoran (12)
University College School

The Night

I sat there at my window,
Thinking about what I should write,
And then . . . it just hit me,
I'd write about the night.

I'd write how it is gloomy,
And not your favourite place to be,
Sometimes it is quite scary,
Particularly when you can't see.

I'd write about the stars,
The way they shine like new,
You feel as though you know them,
And as if they know you.

So when I think more carefully,
I sort of like the night,
The way it keeps its secrets,
And how it keeps me feeling right.

Charlie Wade (12)
University College School

Kew Gardens

Silence, blissful and sweet.
The canopy creating a beautiful umbrella of plants,
The sound of dripping water rippling through the air,
The smell of damp plants rising from the wet, soft earth,
The silhouette of the glistening palms
And the sparkling of sunshine softening the humid heat.
Scattered flowers and leaves on the floor
Making a smell of honey,
Squirrels darting in and out of the towering oaks.
Silence! Peaceful! Sweet!

Ben Bohm-Duchen (11)
University College School